CALL YOURSELF
A TOFFEES FAN?

THE ULTIMATE
EVERTON
QUIZ BOOK

DEDICATION

This book is for two Everton fans who go back a long way in their support of this club. They are Steven Jacques and Clive Coast. In fact, Clive's first Everton experience was at White Hart Lane in October 1958 and we all know what happened there, and it didn't deter him in the least!

ACKNOWLEDGEMENTS

I would like to thank Stuart Tibber for his help in preparing the quiz for publication, and thanks are due again to my editor at Pitch Publishing, Michelle Grainger.

RACING POST

CALL YOURSELF A TOFFEES FAN?

THE ULTIMATE
EVERTON
QUIZ BOOK

MART MATTHEWS

First published by Pitch Publishing on behalf of Racing Post, 2022

Pitch Publishing
Pitch Publishing,
9 Donnington Park,
85 Birdham Road,
Chichester,
West Sussex, PO20 7AJ

www.pitchpublishing.co.uk
info@pitchpublishing.co.uk
www.racingpost.com/shop

A CIP catalogue record is available for this book
from the British Library.

ISBN 9781839501036

Typesetting and origination by Pitch Publishing

Printed and bound in Great Britain by TJ Books Ltd, Padstow

CONTENTS

INTRODUCTION

Greetings all you Evertonians out there, and welcome to what I hope is the most comprehensive quiz on your club you will find. I hope you will pit your wits against other Everton fans with the questions here. A word is required about the League Cup. As with previous volumes in this series, the competition that began life in 1960 as the 'League Cup' will go by that name in this quiz; the only thing constantly looking up who sponsored it at any particular time gives me is a headache!

QUIZ No. 1

ANYTHING GOES – PART 1

1. Which man who played for the club in 76 league games between 1977 and 1979 is the only player to be capped post-war by England with a name ending in the letter 'C'?

2. Who is the Everton manager with the shortest surname?

3. Which member of Manchester United's European Cup-winning side of 1968 later played for Everton?

4. Who is the only Englishman to win a World Cup winner's medal while at Everton?

5. What a hard-luck story! When he joined Everton, the FA Cup trophy was sitting on the sideboard. He left for Arsenal and there it was again in his new club's trophy cabinet. After leaving them, he rocked up at Southampton and sure enough there it was, laughing at him. He never won it. Who was he?

6. Who are the only two England internationals to score against Everton in a post-war FA Cup final?

7. His first name was Mike and he played in 147 league games for Everton in the 1970s. The club now have a player that has dispensed with first names but calls himself by the surname of that 1970s player. What is that surname?

8. Before Frank Lampard's appointment, and discounting caretaker-managers, who was the last Everton manager to be capped by England as a player?

9. He may have played just two games for the club before his move to Reading in 1905, but he was versatile enough to also win the Derby at Epsom in 1975! Who was he?

10. Who is the only car to score against Everton in an FA Cup final?

QUIZ No. 2

ANYTHING GOES - PART 2

1. Who is the only Everton player to score on the first day of the season in five successive years?

2. Which Everton player, who made 177 league appearances for the club between 1913 and 1923 before a move to Preston North End, shares his full name with one of the Beatles?

3. Talking of which, one of the group attended the 1968 FA Cup final between Everton and West Bromwich Albion. Which one?

4. Two years after scoring the winning goal in the 1995 FA Cup final for Everton against Manchester United, Paul Rideout rode out of Goodison to try his luck in a distant country. Which one?

5. Everton's origins are with church football. What church provided the club's original name and what church stands on one corner of Goodison?

6. Jack Southworth ended his superb career at Everton scoring 36 goals in his 31 games for the club after his transfer from Blackburn Rovers in 1893. He did have another string to his bow, though. What was it?

7. Which classy central defender, who was capped 27 times for England, joined Everton from Derby County in 1978 and left for Birmingham City the following year after 32 league games for the Merseysiders?

8. He was born in Birkenhead and joined the Everton ground staff from the juniors in 1951, playing just three games in six years before drifting into non-league football with Tonbridge. He resurrected his career at Gillingham and Portsmouth as a bustling centre-forward before, in his managerial career, bringing Aston Villa their first title for 71 years. Who was he?

9. While we are on the subject of title-winning managers, which player that Everton broke their transfer record to buy in 1950 eventually led Burnley to their last league championship in 1960?

10. The surnames of two leading Everton goalscorers in the immediate post-war years have jazz connections. The top Everton goalscorer of 1946/47 and 1947/48 shares his with the finest New Orleans clarinettist of the 1920s, while the club's top scorer four years running from 1951/52 shares his with the alto sax player who turned jazz on its head in the 1940s. Who are the two players – of football, not jazz?

QUIZ No. 3

ASSORTED OPPONENTS

1. Which country scored for Manchester City at Goodison when they beat Everton 2-1 on 25 April 2009?

2. Which player who shares his surname with a Champions League-winning manager scored for Birmingham City when they knocked Everton out of the FA Cup in the fourth round on 23 January 2010 at Goodison?

3. When Everton drew 2-2 at home to West Ham United on 22 January 2011, one of the visiting players saw a lot of late action. He was shown a yellow card in the 82nd minute, equalised in the 84th minute and was sent off in the 85th. Perhaps he should have minded his Ps and Qs! Who was he?

4. The scorer of Wigan's goal in a 1-1 draw with Everton on 30 April 2011 once had a manager at another club who thought this player had trouble sleeping. Who was the goalscorer?

5. Which colour put through his own net to give Everton a 1-0 win at Sunderland on 12 April 2014?

6. When West Ham United lost 2-1 at home to Everton on 16 May 2015, their goal was scored by a well-known street in the capital. Who scored it?

7. When Southampton beat Everton 3-0 on 20 December 2014 one of their scorers would have been a very great player indeed if he'd only removed one of the letters of his name. Who was he?

8. Which biblical figure scored for Stoke City against Everton when they won 2-0 at home on 4 March 2015?

9. When Everton beat Reading 3-1 on 2 March 2013 the visitors' goal was scored by someone whose surname includes a goalscorer in the FA Cup final replay of 1983 and the scorer of the winning goal in the FA Cup final of 2008. Who scored it?

10. When Everton drew 2-2 at Norwich City on the first day of the 2013/14 season, the home side's equaliser came from someone whose name sounds like a carnivorous mammal sitting in a vehicle eating shellfish! Who was he?

QUIZ No. 4

ASSORTED TOFFEES

1. Gary Lineker lit up Goodison for an all-too-short period in the 1985/86 season. Who were the only club he scored against in both league matches and in the FA Cup?

2. Some clubs aren't lucky enough to get two centre-halves as good as these in their entire history. Collectively they made 586 appearances over a 25-year period for Everton between 1936 and 1961. They share their first name and their surname and are distinguished one from the other by the letters 'E' and 'G' after their first names. Who were they?

3. However great he was, he would always be the second-best centre-forward in Everton's history to most folk in the blue half of the city. He came from Burnley and moved on to Chelsea at the end of the war, but not before he had scored 65 goals in 87 league games. Who was he?

4. Which two Liverpool-born defenders who shared the same surname collectively played 474 times in the league for Everton between 1963 and 1983?

5. Who were the three Evertonians who played in all four FA Cup finals the team were in during the 1980s?

6. That great captain and full-back Warney Cresswell knew how to defend, but he scored just once in the 290 league games he played between 1927 and 1936 and it came away from home in a 4-2 defeat on which major ground?

7. Which player, who went on to score many more, got his goals breakthrough for Everton when he found the net twice against Chelsea in a 3-1 win at Goodison on 19 April 1967?

8. He played over 200 times for the club between 1988 and 1997, scoring his first goal on the opening day of the 1990/91 season at Leeds, and then he opened his FA Cup account with the two that

knocked out Charlton Athletic at The Valley in the third round that same season. Who was he?

9. Who made the finest possible start to his Everton career by scoring his first goal in a 2-0 win against Liverpool on 21 November 1994?

10. On the cover of his excellent book *When footballers were skint*, Jon Henderson has a great photo of this swashbuckling Everton centre-forward in action at Goodison Park. He had two spells with the club and scored 111 goals in all competitions in the 1950s. Who was he?

QUIZ No. 5

AWAY FROM GOODISON - (AFTER)

All these players appeared in FA Cup finals for other clubs after leaving Everton.

1. Everton and Blackburn Rovers did a lot of business with each other in the 1950s and 1960s and the former allowed two players to leave who went on to play 426 league games for Rovers between them, with both appearing in the 1960 final against Wolves. Who were the two players?

2. Which player appeared for Watford on the rather depressing occasion of their heavy defeat by Manchester City in the 2019 final after leaving Goodison Park?

3. Which two members of Spurs' FA Cup-winning side of 1991 had previously played for Everton?

4. Which classy player in the Leeds United team that lost the 1965 final to Liverpool had joined the club from Everton?

5. Which ex-Evertonian was in the Sunderland side that lost to Liverpool in the 1992 final?

6. Which famous Everton captain skippered Arsenal to victory over Liverpool in the 1950 final after being persuaded to leave Goodison?

7. Which Everton midfielder went on to win the FA Cup with Manchester United against Crystal Palace in 2016, and which former blue played a bit further forward in that same team?

8. Which member of Everton's cup finalists of 2009 won the trophy with Manchester City two years later?

9. Which Everton player, who left the club in 1992, won the FA Cup with Arsenal in 1998?

10. Which ex-Evertonian came on as a substitute for Manchester United when they lost to Chelsea in the 2018 final?

QUIZ No. 6

AWAY FROM GOODISON - (BEFORE)

All these players appeared in an FA Cup final for other clubs before they arrived at Everton.

1. Who played for Preston North End in the 1964 FA Cup final against West Ham United before he came to Goodison Park in 1967?

2. Who played for Millwall in the 2004 final against Manchester United before he became an Everton player?

3. Which Southampton player in the 2003 final against Arsenal later signed for Everton?

4. Which member of the Crystal Palace XI at Wembley against Manchester United in the 2016 final ended up at Everton?

5. Which midfielder eventually wound up at Everton after appearances for Manchester City in the cup finals of 2011 and 2013?

6. Which two members of the Spurs side that beat Nottingham Forest in the 1991 FA Cup Final later had spells at Everton?

7. This man damaged Everton in the 1985 final against Manchester United but later became a blue. Who was he?

8. Which Bolton Wanderers inside-forward in their 1958 cup-winning side moved to Goodison in 1962?

9. Which player, who turned out for Manchester City in the 1981 FA Cup Final and replay against Spurs, later played 54 league games for Everton between 1986 and 1988 before retiring?

10. Which defender, who played for Newcastle United against Arsenal in the 1998 final, joined Everton a couple of years later?

QUIZ No. 7

THE 'B' TEAM

All these Everton players' names start with a 'B'. Who are they in each case? All figures are for league games only.

1. 15 games – 2001–02 – joined from Manchester United

2. 74 games – 1995–98 – joined from Aston Villa and left for Sheffield Wednesday

3. 171 games – 1979–85 – joined from Blackburn Rovers and left for Newcastle United

4. 28 games – 1997–2000 – left for West Ham United

5. 76 games – 2005–07 – joined from Southampton and left for Sheffield United

6. 348 games – 2007–20 – joined from Wigan Athletic

7. 19 games – 1994–95 – joined from West Ham United and left for Coventry City

8. 95 games – 1984–89 – joined from Sunderland and left for Sunderland

9. 120 games – 1989–94 – joined from Stoke City and left for Manchester City

10. 131 games – 2013–17 – joined from Manchester City

QUIZ No. 8

BIRTHPLACES

1. Which of these Everton players was the only one not born in a capital city?
   A) Imre Varadi B) Sylvain Distin C) Martin Keown D) Alex Iwobi

2. Which one of these Everton players was not born in Dublin?
   A) Peter Farrell B) Jimmy O'Neill C) Mick Meagan
   D) Seamus Coleman

3. Which one of these Everton players was not born in Glasgow?
   A) Pat Nevin B) Duncan Ferguson C) Andy Gray D) Graeme Sharp

4. Andy Hinchcliffe, Gary Megson, Keith Newton and Phil Jagielka all came from the same city. Which one?

5. Which one of these Everton players was not born in Birmingham?
   A) Mike Bernard B) Bob Latchford C) Lee Carsley D) Joleon Lescott

6. Which cities were the following four Everton players born in?
   A) Tim Cahill B) Alessandro Pistone C) Steven Pienaar
   D) Stuart McCall

7. Which one of these dozen Everton players is not a Liverpudlian?
   Gary Ablett, John Bailey, Leighton Baines. Tom Davies, John Gidman, Alan Harper, Franny Jeffers, Brian Labone, Mike Lyons, Steve McMahon, Johnny Morrissey, James Vaughan

8. Two cities represent the birthplaces of the following four Everton players. What are those two cities?
   Kevin Richardson, Danny Cadamarteri, Fabian Delph, Jimmy Husband

9. Which one of these Evertonians was not born in Belfast?
   A) Billy Bingham B) Darron Gibson C) Bryan Hamilton
   D) Norman Whiteside

10. Everton's current left-sided midfielder who goes by the name Bernard was born in Belo Horizonte in Brazil. What does that name conjure up for older English supporters?

QUIZ No. 9

CAPTAINCY

1. Which Everton captain has won the most league titles and led them out for an FA Cup final the most times?

2. Who is the only man to captain Everton in an FA Cup final this century?

3. The names of the two men who captained Everton to their first two league titles, in 1891 and 1915, have a lot in common. Both their first names begin with a 'J' and they both have four-letter surnames, with the last two being the same and in the same order. Who were these two captains?

4. Which two league-winning Everton captains were also top scorers, in the season they won it?

5. Who led Everton when they met Aston Villa in the League Cup final of 1977?

6. Which man, in the 1960s, experienced both winning and losing an FA Cup final at Wembley as Everton captain?

7. Everton were captained from left-back when they won the league in 1928, and from centre-half when they did it again in 1939. Which two players were involved?

8. Who was the last man to lift the FA Cup over his head for Everton at Wembley?

9. Who was Everton's captain when they won the FA Cup for the first time in 1906?

10. Due to injury, Everton's regular captain was out of the side that won the title in 1970. Who stood in for him, receiving the trophy at Goodison Park on April Fool's Day of that year after a 2-0 win over West Brom?

QUIZ No. 10

COUNTRIES OF ORIGIN - PART 1

In which country were the following Evertonians born?

1. Yerry Mina

2. Richarlison

3. Andre Gomes

4. Gylfi Sigurdsson

5. Moise Kean

6. Brendan Galloway

7. Tim Howard

8. Arouna Kone

9. Bryan Oviedo

10. Johnny Heitinga

QUIZ No. 11

COUNTRIES OF ORIGIN - PART 2

In which country were the following Evertonians born?

1. Lucas Digne

2. Alex Iwobi

3. Muhamed Besic

4. Kevin Mirallas

5. Nikica Jelavic

6. Apostolos Vellios

7. Thomas Gravesen

8. Tomasz Radzinski

9. Gerard Deulofeu

10. Ramiro Funes Mori

QUIZ No. 12

CRYPTIC BLUES - PART 1

You are given the player's league details and a cryptic clue. Can you name them?

1. Married man – 165 games – 1964–73

2. Compass point – 335 games – 1962–75

3. It was unusual for an apple to fall on his head – 49 games – 1969–72

4. And then it happened again! – 76 games – 1970–73

5. There are other things found on trees besides apples and this is one of them – 41 games – 1996–2000

6. You need one of these to play football and fortunately Everton had a spare one as well! – 208 games – 1966–71 and 121 games – 1996–2001

7. Like a needle or a pin! – 322 games – 1980–91

8. A musical and a Scottish football club – 41 games – 1975–77

9. Yorkshire racetrack – 59 games – 1946–51

10. One of two options if you win the toss before a cricket match – 380 games – 1946–59

CRYPTIC BLUES - PART 2

1. Manufacturer of sports equipment – 211 games – 1949–63

2. Member of Ricky Tomlinson's TV family – 232 games – 1966–74

3. Everly brother meets British folk singer – 179 games – 1949–58

4. Current Manchester United midfielder visits small town in Yorkshire – 97 games – 1964–67

5. It doesn't sound like it, but he was no angel! – 256 games – 1960–67

6. Female former player and current TV pundit – 149 games – 1963–67

7. Beatles' producer at Abbey Road – 85 games – 1928–32

8. Footballing brothers visit town in Middlesex – 578 games – 1981–98

9. Merseyside football pools company – 176 games – 1960–65

10. Bob Dylan single about black activist – 75 games – 1934–47

QUIZ No. 14

CRYPTIC BLUES - PART 3

1. A murdered king in *Macbeth* meets Manchester United manager – 239 games – 1994–98 and 2000–2006

2. Pink Floyd's late keyboards man – 60 games – 2002–06

3. It sounds as though he should have played for Accrington! – 52 games – 1979–81

4. London Underground station on the District and Circle line – 232 games – 1956–67

5. Current English golfer – 264 games – 1911–23

6. *Rising Damp* landlord – 14 games – 1919

7. Accomplished painter of horses, born in Liverpool in 1724 – 169 games – 2001–05 and 2006–08

8. Guitar manufacturer – 51 games – 2012–17

9. James Stewart's 6ft-tall rabbit – 320 games – 1962–74

10. Head of a college in the deep south – 399 games – 1925–38

QUIZ No. 15

CRYPTIC BLUES - PART 4

1. Popular 'corner house' cafes between 1909 and 1977 – 389 games – 1969–82

2. Lancastrian football club – 75 games – 1906–08

3. Town in South Wales – 131 games – 2013–17

4. Young goose – 22 games – 2008–10

5. Diane Keaton's character in *The Godfather* – 50 games – 1962–63

6. Hillwalker and writer often to be found in the Lake District – 207 games – 1944–56

7. Handy quality to have, especially for a winger – 58 games – 1996–98

8. Model hires removal company – still at club

9. Where meals get made – 87 games – 1898–1903

10. Irish mustard? – still at club

QUIZ No. 16

EVERTON IN EUROPE 1962-95
- CLUBS

1. Everton played in Europe in 11 seasons over this whole period. In two of their first three years of competition they were drawn against Scottish clubs. Which two were involved?

2. The only time they met a club from their own league came in the Fairs Cup of 1964/65 when they went out to which club?

3. The only time Everton were knocked out by the eventual winners of a tournament came in the European Cup of 1963/64, when they were unlucky enough to get this club in the first round, going down 1-0 on aggregate. Who were they?

4. Which Irish club did Everton beat 5-0 home and away in the UEFA Cup of 1978/79?

5. Which club were the only one to put Everton out of two competitions in this period? In fact, Everton didn't score against them in any of the four games, which came in the UEFA Cup of 1979/80 and the Cup Winners' Cup of 1995/96.

6. The strangest thing about Everton in Europe over this time was that when they won the European Cup Winners' Cup in 1984/85 it was the only time in that decade that they kicked a ball in European competition. Who did they beat 3-1 in that final?

7. The highlight at Goodison over this era was almost certainly the second leg of the semi-final that time in 1984/85, when they beat which club 3-1 after a 0-0 draw in the away leg?

8. In the European Cup of 1970/71, Everton got through one round on penalties after drawing 1-1 home and away, but their luck ran out in the next round at the quarter-final stage when they lost on the away-goals rule. Which two clubs were involved?

9. In the 1966/67 European Cup Winners' Cup, they got through 2-1 on aggregate in the first round against Danish opposition who are almost certainly the first club in the world when it comes to the alphabet. Who were they?

10. Only one city's two teams both knocked Everton out of European competition over this period. Which city was it?

QUIZ No. 17

EVERTON IN EUROPE 1962-95
- PLAYERS

1. Who was Everton's first goalscorer in Europe in a 1-0 win at Goodison Park on 24 October 1962? That slender lead wasn't enough and they went out in the second leg after a 2-0 defeat.

2. Everton's leading European goalscorer over this period had six goals to his name. He was also the only Everton player to score in three successive games in Europe. Who was he?

3. Which defender scored Everton's winner at home to Real Zaragoza when they won 1-0 in the second leg of the second round of the European Cup Winners' Cup of 1966/67? Unfortunately, it wasn't enough as they trailed 2-0 from the first leg.

4. Who scored a Goodison hat-trick when Everton beat Keflavik 6-2 in the first leg of the first round of the European Cup on 16 September 1970?

5. Who was the only player to score from the penalty spot over this period when he found the net away to K.R. Reykjavik in the first leg of the first round of the Cup Winners' Cup of 1995/96?

6. Which Everton wing-half came up with the only goal of the game when Everton beat Nuremburg of Germany in the second leg of the Fairs Cup of 1965/66 to go into the next round after an away 1-1 draw in the first leg?

7. When Everton beat Fortuna Sittard of Holland 3-0 at Goodison in the quarter-final of the Cup Winners' Cup on 6 March 1985, who was responsible for all their goals?

8. Which midfielder in the previous round against Inter Bratislava had given Everton an advantage in the tie by scoring the only goal of the away leg before they completed the job on Merseyside?

9. Which four men who scored for Everton in Europe between 1962 and 1995 also scored for them in an FA Cup final over that same timespan?

10. Among Everton's goalscorers in Europe over this time, whose name was nearest the front of the alphabet and whose name was nearest the back?

QUIZ No. 18

EVERTON IN EUROPE –
THE 21ST CENTURY – CLUBS

1. Everton's participation in European football has usually been patchy and this century has reflected that fact. When they finally got into the Champions League, a false name if ever there was one, they went out at the first opportunity, 4-2 on aggregate, to which Spanish club in 2005/06?

2. Two years later it was the UEFA Cup, the Champions League's ugly cousin, that they were contesting, ending up playing ten games for small reward. Their biggest win was by 6-1 at Goodison in the second leg of the first knock-out round when they beat a team that sound as though they are good at providing roughage for your diet. Who were they?

3. In the next round they were eliminated in the dreaded penalty shoot-out after a 2-2 draw on aggregate against which Italian opponents?

4. They entered the same tournament again the following year but never got past which club in the first round?

5. That wonderful invention known as the Europa League emerged in the 2009/10 season so that people who were struggling to sleep could at least get some help on Thursdays! After a strange play-off against Sigma Olomouc, they managed to get out of their group despite some inconsistent performances. It was a source of some embarrassment that the group winners beat Everton 5-0 and 2-0 when they met. Who were they?

6. In that group, Everton won three and lost three and beat a Greek club 4-0 at home and 1-0 away. Who were they?

7. Who eventually knocked them out in the round-of-32 stage 4-2 on aggregate?

8. Back for more of the same in 2014/15, they progressed from their group after three wins, two draws and a defeat sustained after they had qualified. Which German club did they beat 4-1 at home and 2-0 away?

9. After accounting for Young Boys of Berne in the round of 32, which club accounted for them in the next round 6-4 on aggregate?

10. Returning to the scene of the crime in 2017/18, they had two 1-0 wins in the third qualifying round over Ruzomberok. No, me neither! When they had assured their own exit, they won 3-0 away against Apollon Limassol in their last game. Unfortunately, two poor performances before that against an Italian club who beat them 3-0 and 5-1 had ensured their demise. Who were this Italian side?

QUIZ No. 19

EVERTON IN EUROPE –
THE 21ST CENTURY – PLAYERS

1. Who was Everton's first goalscorer in Europe this century?

2. Who had the shortest name of Everton's goalscorers in Europe over this period? His one and only goal came in a 4-0 Goodison win in the group stage of the 2009/10 Europa League.

3. Which three players scored for Everton from the penalty spot in European competition over these years?

4. Which Everton player scored for the opposition in the UEFA Cup of 2008/09 and then put things right by scoring at the right end in the group stage of the Europa League in 2009/10?

5. Which two players scored hat-tricks in Europe for Everton in this period, the first coming in the 2007/08 UEFA Cup and the second in the Europa League of 2014/15?

6. After earlier goals from Johnson and Jagielka, who got the winner for Everton away to AZ Alkmaar in the group stage of the 2007/08 UEFA Cup?

7. Who was the only player to score for Everton in three successive European matches? He achieved this in the UEFA Cup of 2007/08.

8. Who was Everton's top scorer in Europe over this time with eight goals?

9. Everton drew 1-1 at home to Metalist in the UEFA Cup of 2007/08, and later in that same competition and season they beat Zenit St. Petersburg 1-0, also at home. Both those goals were scored by central defenders. Who were they?

10. Who became the player with the longest surname to score for Everton in Europe in any era when he got the only goal of the away game with AEK Athens in the group stage of the Europa League in 2009/10?

QUIZ No. 20

EVERTON IN THE FA CUP - 1892-1939

1. Few clubs have ever made a more dramatic start to their FA
    Cup story. It came on 18 January 1890. Which club did they
    slaughter 11-2?

2. Naturally, they got knocked out in the next round! Stoke were the
    culprits and became, four years later, the first club to knock Everton
    out of the competition twice. But which club did so in successive
    seasons in 1895 and 1896?

3. By that time Everton had already experienced a losing FA Cup final
    in 1893 and were about to experience another in 1897. As the new
    century dawned, Everton were drawn against the same southern
    club in 1900 and 1901, both times as their first opponent in the
    competition. They lost the first encounter 3-0, but won the second
    3-1, both times away from home. Who did they play?

4. On 28 January 1899, they won first time up 3-1 at home to a small
    town in the North East that became famous overnight 30 years later
    with a march to London to protest against their living conditions.
    Who were they?

5. You could say that Everton's tie at home to Southampton on
    3 March 1905 was settled in their favour 4-0. Why?

6. Three Everton players with names beginning with 'B' scored hat-
    tricks in the competition. The first came against Southport in 1895,
    the second against Oldham in 1908 and the third against Bury in
    1912, the last two being four-timers. Which three players were on
    the mark?

7. Everton's first taste of FA Cup success came in 1906 but has been
    covered elsewhere. Perhaps their most embarrassing FA Cup
    moment came on 7 January 1922, when they lost 6-0 at home to a
    club from a lower division that, 11 years before, they had beaten 4-0
    in London at the same stage of the competition. Which club carried
    out the humiliation?

8. Dixie Dean appeared on the scene in the mid-1920s and was to become their record goalscorer in the competition and a key figure in their 1933 success. His first FA Cup goal came in a 1-1 draw at Goodison Park in the third round on 9 January 1925 against which London club?

9. When Everton beat Grimsby Town 6-3 in the third round at Goodison on 12 January 1935, they were helped by a hat-trick from Albert Geldard, who had already made a name for himself with his previous club, Bradford Park Avenue. How?

10. In the final season before World War Two brought an end to proceedings, the Goodison crowd were proclaiming a new centre-forward who had burst on to the scene two years earlier. In the fourth round, on 21 January 1939, he scored four of Everton's goals in an 8-0 win over Doncaster Rovers. Who was he?

QUIZ No. 21

EVERTON IN THE FA CUP - 1945-60

1. The FA Cup returned a year before the league got under way and for the only time in its history was a two-leg affair. Everton lost in the third round 4-3 on aggregate to which club from Lancashire?

2. In 1946/47 they were knocked out at the fourth-round stage by the same team and the same score as in an FA Cup final they had contested some 40 years before. Who repeated the feat by beating them again?

3. In the sixth round in 1952/53, Dave Hickson's goal away from home gave Everton a 1-0 win against a club he was to join briefly two years later. Who were they?

4. For the only time in this period, in 1957/58 and 1958/59, Everton were drawn against the same club in the third round in successive seasons, beating them 3-1 after a replay on the first occasion and 4-0 on the second. Who were they?

5. Everton beat two clubs twice over this period without the need of a replay and without losing against them, one of them from London and the other from the South East. A clue would be that at this time fans of the London club would often go to the other club on their holidays. Who were the two clubs?

6. Who was Everton's top scorer in the competition over this period with 16 goals?

7. Which two clubs knocked Everton out of the FA Cup more than once in this 15-year period?

8. Over this time Everton contrived to draw away with two London clubs from a lower division and then lose the replay at Goodison. They did this in the fifth round in 1947/48 and the third round in 1951/52. Which two clubs knocked them out?

9. Which Lancastrians did they beat in the third round in 1956/57 and then lose to in the fourth round the following year?

10. The FA Cup of 1949/50 brought a unique situation when Everton dismissed three London clubs in succession from the competition, the first from the west of the capital, the second from the east and the third from the north. Which three clubs were involved?

QUIZ No. 22

EVERTON IN CUP COMPETITIONS – THE 1960s

1. Which Yorkshire club were the first to knock Everton out of the FA Cup at the start of the decade in the third round of the 1960/61 season and the last to do so at the end of the decade at the same stage in 1969/70?

2. Everton met 24 opponents in the FA Cup over the decade but only one from the capital, who beat them 1-0 in the fifth round on 16 March 1963. Who were they?

3. Two clubs ended Everton's hopes in both the FA Cup and the League Cup over the decade, with one of them beating Everton on their way to winning both competitions. Who were the two clubs?

4. Everton met two non-league sides in the FA Cup, the first in a 4-0 win at Goodison in the third round on 6 January 1962, and the second in the fourth round on their way to winning the trophy in 1966, when they beat the non-league club 3-0 away. Who were the two teams?

5. Everton entered the new League Cup competition in its first season but then ducked it for the next seven years. In that first season, they beat neighbours Tranmere Rovers 4-0 at Prenton Park on 21 December 1960. Who scored a hat-trick in that game?

6. Which club did Everton put out of the League Cup 5-0 on their own ground in the 1967/68 season and then do the same to them 1-0 at Goodison in the FA Cup in the following season?

7. Who scored Everton's winning goal in the 1968 FA Cup semi-final?

8. In 1964/65 Everton didn't get far in the FA Cup but nevertheless played four times against two Yorkshire clubs, Sheffield Wednesday and Leeds United, losing to the latter after a replay. Which Everton player found the net in all four games?

9. Which Everton forward scored in the FA Cup three years in a row from 1961/62 to 1963/64?

10. In that inaugural League Cup season of 1960/61, Everton played five clubs, none of which were from their own division, eventually going out of the competition disappointingly at Shrewsbury when they had a good chance to be the first club to win it. A strange feature was that they won their first three games by the same score, against Accrington Stanley, Walsall and Bury. What was that score?

EVERTON IN CUP COMPETITIONS – THE 1970s

1. Everton reached an FA Cup semi-final in 1971 and 1980. What was strange about their progress to those two semi-finals?

2. Everton's only non-league opposition in the FA Cup gave the Merseysiders a real scare by drawing 1-1 at Goodison Park on 4 January 1975, before Everton came good in the replay with a 2-0 win. Who were that opposition?

3. Which London club did they win and lose to in the League Cup over this decade?

4. Which two clubs from the same city caused Everton's League Cup exit, the first in 1975/76 and the second in 1978/79?

5. Which northern club did Everton play in both competitions in the 1977/78 season, losing in the FA Cup and going through after a replay in the League Cup?

6. Everton were particularly vulnerable to London clubs in the FA Cup, going out to one on four occasions, but never in London itself. Which four clubs did the damage, three times at Goodison and once at a neutral ground?

7. However, in the 1978/79 season there was one London club that got an almighty mauling at Goodison when they lost a League Cup tie by 8-0. Who were they?

8. It's hard to believe but Everton played nine matches over the two competitions against one particular club, winning three, drawing four and losing two. Who were this team?

9. Who, in 1977, were the only club in the decade to meet Everton in a League Cup semi-final?

10. In the 1977/78 season Everton knocked out of the League Cup two teams from the same city, both away from home, by 3-0 and 3-1. What was that city?

QUIZ No. 24

EVERTON IN CUP COMPETITIONS – THE 1980s

1. Which two clubs beginning with the same letter did Everton play in League Cup semi-finals over this decade?

2. Which Welsh club were Everton drawn against in two two-leg League Cup affairs in 1982/83 and 1986/87, scoring 13 goals against three in the four matches?

3. Which black-and-white-striped team had knocked Everton out of the League Cup in 1979/80 and then did it again in 1984/85?

4. Which two London clubs that begin with the same letter put paid to Everton's FA Cup hopes in 1981/82 and 1986/87?

5. 18 January 1984 has gone down as a pivotal night in Everton folklore. All they did was get a late equaliser in an away League Cup tie, but it probably saved a manager's job who produced great success later for the club. Who were they playing, who scored the vital goal and which manager clung on to his job?

6. In the 1980s Everton received significant assistance from their opponents in the two domestic cup competitions. They scored eight own goals for the Toffees, with one club providing one in each competition. It was the club that Everton's stalwart wing-half Cyril Lello came from in 1948 before playing 237 league games for the Merseysiders. Does that make it any easier to identify which club scored those own goals?

7. Which club did Everton play four times in League Cup matches and lose only one?

8. Everton were a superb side in the mid-to-late 1980s but frustration accompanied their success. Nowhere was this better illustrated than in the FA Cup of 1987/88. They played seven games to get past two opponents. Three of them were against Middlesbrough. They played out three 1-1 draws against the other club before crazily settling it by winning 5-0 on their ground. Who were this club?

9. Who scored a hat-trick in that 5-0 win?

10. Then, utterly exhausted by all that effort to gain such little ground, who was waiting to have them for lunch in the next round, their eighth game in the competition? The horror!

QUIZ No. 25

EVERTON IN CUP COMPETITIONS – THE 1990s

1. Everton's best moment in this decade was their FA Cup win in 1995. A feature of their success was that they conceded just one goal in the six matches it took to win it, and that came from the penalty spot in the semi-final. Which player scored it?

2. Allowing for an apostrophe, Everton's last FA Cup tie of 1998/99 and their first one the following year were played against two clubs on two grounds with the same name. Who were their two opponents?

3. Everton beat one club away in two FA Cup seasons. Firstly, they won 1-0 in a fourth-round tie the year they went on to win the trophy, and then they won there again by 2-0 in the third round of 1998/99. Who did they beat?

4. Which London club knocked Everton out of both competitions during this decade, in the FA Cup of 1991/92 and the League Cup of 1992/93?

5. On 11 November 1998 Everton experienced a penalty shoot-out in the League Cup for the first time, after a 1-1 draw at Goodison. Which club beat them 6-5 in the shoot-out?

6. Everton's top League Cup goalscorer over the decade was an attacking midfielder, while their top FA Cup goalscorer was an out-and-out striker. Who were the two men?

7. Everton scored five times in an FA Cup tie once during the decade. It came on 18 February 1995 in the fifth round at Goodison. Who did they beat?

8. Everton's first two games of the decade in the League Cup brought them an 11-0 aggregate win over which club beginning with a 'W' before they fell at the next hurdle at Bramall Lane?

9. It turned out that the first two teams they accounted for in the competition the following season also began with a 'W'. Who were they?

10. In 1994/95, 1995/96 and 1996/97 Everton were acutely embarrassed by being dismissed in successive seasons from the League Cup by teams from a lower division. In reality it happened five times over the ten years! In the three years listed, they went out to a club on the south coast, a London club and a club from Yorkshire. Who were they?

QUIZ No. 26

EVERTON IN THE LEAGUE - 1888-1939

1. Everton were one of the celebrated 12 that literally kicked off proceedings on 8 September 1888. They won their first game 2-1 at home to the club that were alphabetically first of the 12. Who were they and where did the game take place?

2. One Midlands club were given some heavy beatings in the early years of the league by Everton. Between 1888 and 1893 they lost 6-2, 7-0, 6-2 again, 6-1 and 5-0. Who were they?

3. Everton won the league five times in this period, beginning in 1890/91, its third season of competition. Which club, in finishing second to Everton that season, were failing to win it for the first time?

4. As World War One neared, Everton completed another league title in 1914/15. This time the runners-up were a club from Lancashire that still haven't won anything in the game. With just a couple more points, they would have done. Who were they?

5. The London club that constituted Everton's last opponent before the war were also their first opponents after it, on 30 August 1919. Who were they?

6. What strange characteristic embodied the fixture list for the first five seasons after the war?

7. Everton were scoring goals for fun in the late 1920s and early 1930s and the title came their way again in one of the most celebrated seasons of all, that of 1927/28. How many games in a row from the start of the season did Dixie Dean score in?

8. Incredibly, within two years of that title Everton were relegated, but they wasted little time feeling sorry for themselves by bouncing back at the first time of asking and winning the Second Division. The club that came up with them as runners-up also won the FA Cup that year, a double that had not been done before and hasn't been repeated since. Who were they?

It is of note that Dixie Dean stayed with the club after relegation and worked to get them back. You would be unlikely to see that today, despite the many ludicrous loyalty bonuses on offer.

9. The following season, Everton emulated Liverpool's achievement of a quarter of a century before by winning the title in their first season up with the big boys. 116 goals were scored, 84 of them coming at Goodison Park. At one point in that season, how many games in succession at home did it take them to score 43 goals?

10. It could be taken as a worrying sign that when Everton landed the league title there was a war about to break out. Just like the 'first lot', as the troops referred to the 1914–18 conflict, Everton won their fifth title in 1938/39. This put them third in the pecking order at that point in the league's history, behind which two clubs who had each won it six times?

QUIZ No. 27

EVERTON IN THE LEAGUE 1946-60

1. These were the lost years. When they won the league in 1939, nobody expected them to keep the trophy for the next six years, so although their fall from grace was artificially slowed down by the war, when it came they descended from the mountain top a lot quicker than anyone expected. But let's keep the doom and gloom for later. Who scored Everton's first league hat-trick of the post-war era in a 4-2 win over Sunderland at Goodison on 15 February 1947 and followed up on 5 March 1949 with a four-timer in a 5-0 win over Blackpool on the same ground?

2. In the period between August and November of 1948, Everton sustained 11 defeats in 15 games. In those 11 matches they conceded 34 goals. How many did they score?

3. In the 1949/50 season their goalkeeper Ted Sagar missed one game. It was on a long journey south and they returned beaten 7-0. Just for good measure, the same club beat them 5-1 and 6-3 the following season as well. Who were they?

4. This couldn't go on forever. After two seasons of missing the drop by three places, the axe fell in the 1950/51 season. After six games in March without scoring a single goal, they went to Sheffield Wednesday on the final day needing a draw to survive. What happened?

5. When they were relegated in 1929/30, they came back straight away. This was tougher. Their first season in the Second Division yielded seventh spot and this was deemed about as bad as it could be. However, 1952/53 was worse. In fact, finishing 16th in the second tier constituted their worst season ever. Along the way they also got caned 8-2 by which Yorkshire club?

6. The only bit of comfort came with a great individual scoring performance on 27 September 1952 in a 7-1 win over Doncaster Rovers. Who netted five goals that day?

7. In 1953/54 they finally redeemed themselves by gaining promotion with Leicester City, who edged them out of the title on goal average. In an incredible February that's produced nothing like it since, they won 6-2 at Derby, 6-1 at home to Brentford, and then, with the Goodison attendance nearly double that of the previous win, beat Plymouth Argyle by a very rare scoreline indeed. What was it?

8. Things looked good when their first game back in the top flight ended with a 5-2 win in Yorkshire and they ended the season in mid-table. However, that was as good as it got, and the rest of this period was characterised by mediocrity, with three 15th-placed finishes and two 16th. Who was that win in Yorkshire against that proved a false dawn?

9. The side did have goals in them, but the defence was non-existent on occasion. The perfect example was a famous fixture in London on 11 October 1958 when they lost 10-4. Who beat them, and which Everton player came off the field with a hat-trick against his name?

10. In this period, they were regularly hammered. For example, in 1959/60 Leicester City, Nottingham Forest and Chelsea all beat Everton 6-1. Their poor performances continued to the very end of the season, with a 5-0 defeat at Old Trafford. Before that, on 7 November 1959, they shipped another eight, going down 8-2 to which northern club?

QUIZ No. 28

EVERTON IN THE LEAGUE - THE 1960s

1. The 1960s were supposed to be about change, or so Sam Cooke told us. Everton certainly needed some and it didn't take too long arriving. In 1960/61 their fifth-place finish was ten places better than anything they had managed for several years. It didn't stop manager Johnny Carey being sacked in April, after three wins and a draw in his previous four games. He sat in the stands on 15 April 1961 as his side won 5-1 against Cardiff City, with fans letting chairman John Moores know what they thought of his decision. Which Everton player scored a hat-trick in the game?

2. Harry Catterick took over and was immediately successful. If they had won at Ipswich, instead of losing, they would have been one point off the title in his first full season of 1961/62. The last home game of the season was a memorable affair, when they signed off with an 8-3 win against which club?

3. The title was delivered in 1962/63, clinched with a 12-match unbeaten run. They scored two goals for every one they conceded and the key was the defence. Not since 1911/12 had they let in this number of goals. How many?
A) 38 B) 40 C) 42 D) 44

4. In 1963/64 they would have denied Liverpool the title if they had won their last three away games instead of losing them. Which centre-forward had a dream debut at Goodison Park, scoring a hat-trick in a 6-1 Everton win over Nottingham Forest on 14 March 1964?

5. In 1965/66 they sunk to 11th but won the FA Cup. The next season had an underwhelming start, with two wins from the first seven games. The next game was a nine-goal thriller against West Brom at Goodison. How did it turn out?

6. In 1967/68 they finished fifth. The last game at Goodison Park was won 5-1 against a London club who were relegated and therefore not party to the traditional end-of-season rapport with the fans that such fixtures produce. Who were they?

7. Joe Royle announced himself to the Goodison faithful the year before, but on 30 November 1968 he scored a hat-trick in front of them in a 7-1 win over which Midlands club?

8. 1969/70 brought the title back to Goodison after an eight-match winning run in March and April. The most enthralling game was a feisty affair early on in the season when Everton beat Leeds United 3-2 on Merseyside. Their scorers sound like the Duke of Edinburgh. Why?

9. At the start of the decade, one player was Everton's top league goalscorer four years running, and after that three players won it twice in a row. Who were the four men?

10. Which two goalkeepers had at least one season when they didn't miss a league game?

QUIZ No. 29

EVERTON IN THE LEAGUE - THE 1970s

1. After the great years of the 1960s, this decade was a massive disappointment in which they never once came close to winning the league. The signs were there in the first season. Their 4-1 win at Goodison Park on 12 December 1970 was the only time that season they scored four times in a game. Who did they beat?
    A) Chelsea B) Huddersfield Town C) Newcastle United
    D) Southampton

2. In 1971/72, incredibly, they scored more than a fifth of their goals for the whole season in one game! Those goals came at Goodison on 20 November 1971 in an 8-0 win over Southampton and made up for the 18 times they failed to score in the league. Seven of the eight came from just two players. Who were they?

3. Goalscoring remained a problem as the decade wore on, but, after ending up 14th, 15th, 17th and seventh, they did manage fourth place in 1974/75. Who scored more than twice as many league goals as any other player that season?

4. 1977/78 was their best season of the decade, their third-place finish being helped by two excellent 5-1 wins on their travels, one in the Midlands and the other in London. Who were the beaten clubs?

5. Bob Latchford got four against the London club and also scored in the other match. Which other Everton player scored in both games?

6. Goodison Park saw a couple of big wins too in that season, when Coventry City in November and Chelsea on the last day of the season went down heavily by the same score. What was it?
    A) 5-0 B) 6-0 C) 5-1 D) 6-1

7. 10 February 1979 brought a hat-trick in a 4-1 win at Goodison for Andy King. Who were the visitors?

8. After a fourth-place finish in 1978/79, Everton ended the decade close to relegation in 1979/80, winning just nine of their 42 matches. After one win in nine games, Everton were grateful on 13 November 1979 for Bob Latchford's hat-trick contribution to a 5-1 win over which Yorkshire club at Goodison Park?

9. Three Everton goalkeepers played every league game in a season. They were Gordon West, David Lawson and George Wood. Which one of the three did it twice?

10. Five outfield players also played every game in a season. They were Martin Dobson, Mike Lyons, Ken McNaught, Andy King and John Bailey. Which one of these performed the feat twice?

QUIZ No. 30

EVERTON IN THE LEAGUE - THE 1980s

1. In the 1980s Everton were an average side at the start and finish of the decade but a brilliant one in the middle, when they twice won the league and when just one more goal at Goodison against Liverpool on 21 September 1985 would have given them three league titles in a row. On 20 September 1980 they won 5-0 at home, and then won away by the same score one week later. The two beaten clubs began with the letter 'C'. Who were they?

2. 1981/82 was characterised by the fact that no club scored more than three against Everton, and Everton repeated that pattern in their goals tally too. More goals arrived in 1982/83, when they beat Villa 5-0 early on, but which club did Everton beat 5-0 at home and 5-1 away that season?
    A) Brighton & Hove Albion B) Coventry City C) Luton Town
    D) Swansea City

3. On 25 February 1984 Everton were involved in a thrilling 4-4 draw away from home. Then, on 29 September of the same year, they went back to the same ground and won 5-4. What was the ground?

4. It all came good in 1984/85, when the title returned to Goodison Park for the first time in 15 years, despite losing their opening two games. The whole thing hinged on an amazing run from Boxing Day to May, when they were undefeated in 18 matches. How many did they win?

5. Which two clubs, one from the Midlands and the other a bit further north, tasted 5-0 defeats at Goodison Park in the league that season?

6. Everton were runners-up in 1985/86 in a season in which two southern clubs were caned 6-1 at Goodison. If you need a clue: they have met each other in an FA Cup final in the current century. Who are they?

7. You couldn't keep this team down for long and they took the title again in 1986/87. There was just one hat-trick by an Everton player all season and it came at Goodison on 20 April 1987 in a 3-0 win over Newcastle United. Who scored it?

8. In 1987/88 the defence was as good as ever, but they scored 23 fewer goals and finished fourth. Graeme Sharp had a field day on 3 October 1987 when he got all the goals in Everton's 4-0 away win. On which ground?
    A) Carrow Road B) The Dell C) Loftus Road D) Upton Park

9. What was Everton's average league position over this decade?

10. They ended the decade in sixth place and in the two league games with one particular club they shared 14 goals. Everton lost 6-2 away to them and then closed the season with a 3-3 home draw with the same Midlands team. Who were they?

QUIZ No. 31

EVERTON IN THE LEAGUE – THE 1990s

1. This was a difficult decade for Everton fans, apart from that day at Wembley in the middle of it. In how many of the ten seasons did Everton finish in the top half?

2. I was at Villa Park on 30 March 1991 to see a Polish player score his first goal for Everton in a 2-2 draw against Aston Villa. Who was he?

3. Everton recorded successive home wins on 21 September 1991 and 5 October 1991, beating Coventry City 3-0 and Spurs 3-1. With the aid of a penalty in each instance, which two players got hat-tricks?

4. It was typical of Everton to turn in a big performance after a mediocre season when it had long ceased to matter. The season's final game, on 8 May 1993, produced out of the blue a 5-2 away win. Which northern club did they beat?

5. In the 1993/94 season Tony Cottee scored Goodison hat-tricks in wins by 4-2 and 6-2 against two sides beginning with the same letter who were both relegated at the end of the season. Who were they?

6. Things got very gut-wrenching towards the end of that season when they needed to win their last game to stay up. From a terrible start to the game, they finally got the job done 3-2. Who were they playing and which two players got the vital goals between them?

7. Although they tasted cup glory in 1994/95, they failed to score in 16 league matches that season. Things improved in 1995/96 because they scored 20 more goals and, despite winning just two of their first 11 games, they finished sixth. Which new man's pace and goals made the difference and led to him being their leading goalscorer that season?

8. In 1996/97 the extra 20 goals had disappeared again, but they did have one field day when a Gary Speed hat-trick prompted a 7-1 win at Goodison on 16 November 1996 against which southern club?

9. It was another tight affair at the bottom in 1997/98, when they stayed up on goal difference. Duncan Ferguson's hat-trick won a home game 3-2 on 28 December 1997 and the club they beat that day would have stayed up and relegated Everton if the Everton centre-forward had scored one fewer goal. Which team were relegated alongside Barnsley and Crystal Palace?

10. On the first April Fool's Day of the new millennium, Everton beat Watford 4-2 at Goodison Park and two of their goals came from players with the same surname who were scoring their only goals for the club that day. Who were they?

QUIZ No. 32

EVERTON V LIVERPOOL – LEAGUE AND FA CUP 1894-1939

1. Everton won their first three home games against Liverpool, starting in 1894, by 3-0, 2-1 and 3-0 again. All their wins came in the same month of the year. Which one?

2. Over the nearly half a century that this section deals with, the two clubs played seven times against each other in the FA Cup. Two of those seven were drawn. Which club shaded the other five by three to two?

3. Dixie Dean's superb record against Liverpool in the league is dealt with elsewhere for the most part, but he scored just once in the FA Cup against them. It came on 19 January 1932. The game ended 2-1 to which team and was it at Anfield or Goodison?

4. Liverpool were the April Fools on the first day of that month in 1904, when their 5-2 defeat at Goodison Park contributed to their relegation at the end of the season. Which Everton player became the first man to score four goals in the Merseyside derby in that game?

5. The first FA Cup semi-final meeting between the clubs came on 31 March 1906, with Everton winning 2-0 on the way to their first FA Cup final victory. Where was the game played?

6. We won't mention the score, but the highest number of goals in a Merseyside derby came on 11 February 1933 at Anfield. How many?

7. Having won 5-0 against the Reds in 1909 at Goodison, five years later they repeated the feat at Anfield, with the help of a hat-trick from which player?

8. In 1926, 1928 and 1930 the clubs gave the fans great entertainment with three draws by the same score, the one at Anfield sandwiched by two at Goodison. What was that score?

9.   When Everton won 3-0 at Anfield against Liverpool on 7 September 1929, if you put their two scorers together they produce a mate of Frank Sinatra. Who scored the goals that day?

10. Who scored four times against Liverpool in the last two league seasons before World War Two brought an end to the derby for several years?

QUIZ No. 33

EVERTON V LIVERPOOL - CUP COMPETITIONS 1946-90

This is not a section of the quiz that any Evertonian is looking forward to, so my questions are designed to dull the pain somewhat. Have a stiff drink and give it a go!

1. Everton and Liverpool met 13 times over this period, ten times in the FA Cup and three times in the League Cup. How many did Everton win?

2. The FA Cup competition consists for the bigger clubs of rounds three to six, a semi-final and final. Which two of those rounds did they not play each other in?

3. Who is the only Everton player to score for Everton against Liverpool in more than one FA Cup tie in this period?

4. Who is the only Everton player to score more than once in an FA Cup game against Liverpool in this period?

5. Of the following five venues in this period, which is the only one that Liverpool have not beaten Everton on?
   A) Anfield B) Goodison Park C) Maine Road D) Old Trafford
   E) Wembley

6. On 23 March 1977 Everton and Liverpool met in an FA Cup semi-final at Maine Road that ended in a 2-2 draw. Everton scored what looked like the winner in that game but the referee ruled it out for a dubious handball. Who had put the ball in the net and which referee had ensured himself undying hatred from the blue half of the city?

7. Everton's scorers in that game were a Scottish international who was born in Aldershot and someone who sounds extremely Scottish but was born in Grimsby. Who were the two men?

8. Who was the only Everton goalscorer in a cup tie against Liverpool in this period to eventually get his hands on an FA Cup winner's medal?

9. Everton beat Liverpool 2-1 in the FA Cup fourth round on 24 January 1981 at Goodison. The name of one of their goalscorers starts with the first letter of the club, and the name of the other scorer starts with the second letter of the club. Who were the two men?

10. A tough one to finish. Those two Everton goalscorers in the previous question moved about a bit in their careers, each of them playing for eight clubs. Besides Everton, which Midlands club was the only club they both played for?

QUIZ No. 34

EVERTON V LIVERPOOL – CUP COMPETITIONS 1990-2020

1. Everton acquitted themselves better in this period than the last. The Merseyside rivals met for the first time on 17 February 1991 at Anfield and drew 0-0, the only talking point being why Everton didn't get a penalty when Ablett brought down which Everton player?

2. The replay at Goodison three days later produced the most exciting game between the clubs for many years when Everton refused to lie down, coming back in the 90 minutes and again in extra time to force a 4-4 draw. The same player's goals sent the game into extra time and produced the leveller at the end of that extra time. Who was he?

3. Who scored Everton's first two goals and which future Evertonian did the same for the visitors?

4. When they had another go at deciding the outcome on 27 February at Goodison, Everton finally got their noses in front for the first time in the tie, winning 1-0 through whose goal in the 12th minute?

5. When they next met in the FA Cup it was on 25 January 2009 at Anfield and produced a 1-1 draw. Whose goal put Everton in front in the game?

6. The replay on 4 February was a nailbiter that went to extra time. Whose goal two minutes from the end won the tie for Everton?

7. It was a great experience for Evertonians in the ground. Why was it less so for those watching on television?

8. In 2012 the two clubs met in yet another FA Cup semi-final, with the Reds coming out on top 2-1. Who scored Everton's goal?

9. Unfortunately that same scoreline prevailed when they next met in the FA Cup third round on 5 January 2018. Who was the Toffees' goalscorer on this occasion?

10. The last time they met was another third-round tie in 2020, which Liverpool won 1-0. So much for the FA Cup, but which club had the edge in the League Cup over this period?

QUIZ No. 35

EVERTON V LIVERPOOL - THE LEAGUE 1946-1990

1. There had been great expectation before the first Everton v Liverpool game after World War One, in 1919. Now that expectation attached itself to the first game between the clubs after World War Two that took place at Anfield on 21 September 1946. Both those games ended with the same score. What was it?

2. Which Everton forward scored their first goal against Liverpool after the war when he came up with the winner at Goodison Park on 29 January 1947?

3. Even more expectation was involved on 22 September 1962 for a match that ended 2-2 at Goodison. It was the first meeting between the sides for eight long years. Which Everton player scored in that game and home and away against the old enemy the following season as well?

4. The 1964/65 season produced happy memories of the derby for Evertonians when they won 2-1 at home and 4-0 away. A singer and a religious building scored in both these games for Everton. Who were they?

5. When Everton beat Liverpool 3-1 at Goodison on 27 August 1966, their goals came from two players with surnames beginning with a 'B'. Who were they?

6. When Everton won the league in 1970, they won 2-0 at Anfield. In the following season they lost 3-2 there, but the same two players who'd scored their goals in the earlier game were on the mark again. Who were they?

7. In 1968 Everton beat Liverpool 1-0 at Goodison and then in 1978 repeated the trick. The scorers of the winning goals in each game have a surname beginning with the same letter. Who are they?

8. What was unique about league meetings between the clubs in the 1974/75 season?

9. Everton had two more 1-0 Goodison wins over Liverpool in the 1980s. The first came for the team about to lift the league trophy on 23 May 1985, while the second occurred on 20 March 1988. Which two players got those winning goals?

10. Whose wonder strike at Anfield on 20 October 1984 gave the visitors a 1-0 win and sent Evertonians into ecstasy?

QUIZ No. 36

EVERTON V LIVERPOOL –
THE LEAGUE 1990-2020

1. Everton had not won a Merseyside derby in eight attempts in the league when Liverpool visited on 7 December 1992. Everton won the game 2-1. Which two players scored their goals?

2. The Toffees won the next two Goodison derbies as well, before, in the 1995/96 season, drawing 1-1 at Goodison and winning 2-1 at Anfield. One player scored all three of their goals. Who was he?

3. In the last match of the millennium between the clubs, Everton won 1-0 at Anfield on 27 September 1999. Who scored the vital goal?

4. Who scored Everton's winner against Liverpool when the home side won 1-0 on 11 December 2004?

5. Everton registered their biggest win over Liverpool in this period on 9 September 2006 at Goodison Park. What was that score?

6. Which two players in blue scored when Liverpool were defeated 2-0 at Goodison on 17 October 2010?

7. On 23 November 2013 the clubs played out a 3-3 draw at Goodison when Everton were denied victory through a last-minute goal from Sturridge. Lukaku scored two of Everton's three goals. Who got the other one?

8. Which Everton player stunned the Kop with a tremendous goal in the 92nd minute to earn a 1-1 draw at Anfield on 27 September 2014?

9. Who scored from the penalty spot for Everton in another 1-1 Anfield draw on 10 December 2017?

10. The 2019/20 Goodison encounter, postponed from March because of Covid, was long awaited despite there being not even a man and his dog in the old place when it finally happened on 21 June 2020. What was the score?

QUIZ No. 37

EVERTONIANS

All the following are Everton fans. Can you name them in each case?

1. It's been 'a fine romance' between this famous English actress and Everton Football Club for many years now.

2. This late scouse comic played Harry Cross in *Brookside* and couldn't have a more perfect name for an Everton fan.

3. Derby-winning jockey aboard Sir Percy at Epsom in 2006.

4. Rugby Union player who doubles as a car!

5. It sounds like this veteran disc jockey supports another team from the North West, but apparently he's a toffee lover.

6. Merseyside boxing champion who stepped out of the ring in 2018.

7. Actor who played in goal in a team with Bobby Moore and Russell Osman when he might have liked to play with Joe-Max Moore and Leon Osman.

8. Joe Royle had his 'dogs of war', whereas hers were of the straw variety.

9. Snooker-playing bird.

10. His name suggests he should have kept the job, but the Beatles' management thought otherwise.

QUIZ No. 38

EVERTON - SEASON 2000/01

1. The new century started with another poor season, just like the four that had ended the previous one! However, there was some joy to be garnered from the season's first home game when which player announced his return to Goodison with two of the three goals that sunk Charlton Athletic?

2. Who scored for the Toffees in four successive league games between 23 August and 9 September?

3. In consecutive weeks at Goodison, on 18 and 25 November, Everton beat Arsenal 2-0 and Chelsea 2-1. Two men who share the first letter of their surnames scored the goals in both games. Who were they?

4. David Unsworth scored five goals from the full-back position, two of them in consecutive away games in London and the Midlands against two teams that share the same colours. Who were they?

5. The domestic cup competitions could hardly have been more depressing. Which club from the west of the country put paid to their League Cup hopes 4-2 on penalties after two 1-1 draws in their two-leg meeting?

6. If anything, it was even worse in the FA Cup because the humiliation had a local edge to it. After seeing off Watford in the third round, who beat them 3-0 at Goodison in the next round?

7. Who, despite not reaching double figures, was Everton's top league goalscorer?

8. Which central defender missed just one league game all season and scored in the 3-1 win over Manchester City on 8 April 2001?

9. Besides Old Trafford, what was the only other away ground to attract over 50,000 for the visit of Everton?

10. Everton drew just one of their 19 away games. It came in the Midlands with a 1-1 scoreline on 23 September 2000. Who were their hosts?

QUIZ No. 39

EVERTON - SEASON 2001/02

1. Everton's progress in relation to the previous season was one point and one place, which puts one in mind of the piece of earth on the table in *Blackadder*! Duncan Ferguson was top league goalscorer, but you had to divide Dixie Dean's best total by ten to produce the number he scored. How many was it?

2. I don't know if this is a good thing, but I suspect not. Everton equalled a club record for the number of players scoring for them in the league in a season when how many did so?

3. Who scored his one and only Everton goal on 12 January in a 1-0 home win over Sunderland?

4. In the League Cup Everton's exit came by a penalty shoot-out at the first hurdle, as it had the season before. Which London club put them out of the competition?

5. They had a decent run in the FA Cup that accounted for Stoke City, Leyton Orient and Crewe Alexandra before going out at the sixth-round stage to which club from the North East by 3-0?

6. Which manager was, as they say, relieved of his duties after that game?

7. Whose three FA Cup goals made him Everton's top scorer in the competition?

8. The season's biggest win came on 29 September when which London club were beaten 5-0 at Goodison Park?

9. Everton did the league 'double' over two clubs. Derby County, beaten 4-3 and 1-0, were one of them, but the other was the only team not to register a goal against Everton, going down 2-0 and 1-0. Who were they?

10. One man, towards the end of the 19th century, and another who shared his surname, in the 1920s, between them scored 165 goals for Everton in all competitions. In the 2001/02 season someone resurrected that surname from Everton's history by scoring three times in five games at the end of the season. Who was he?

QUIZ No. 40

EVERTON - SEASON 2002/03

1. Under David Moyes, Everton moved into the top half of the table at last. The opening day of the season saw them draw 2-2 at home with Spurs. Which Everton player, who had joined the club from Sheffield Wednesday, scored his last goal for the home side in that game?

2. The key thing about this season was that it brought hope for the future in the shape of Wayne Rooney. Against which League Cup opponent did he become Everton's youngest-ever goalscorer in a 3-0 away win on 1 October 2002?

3. In the next round, Everton reversed the pattern of the previous two years and actually won a penalty shoot-out after a 3-3 away draw. Who did they eliminate on penalties?

4. The run was ended abruptly with a 4-1 defeat at which London club?

5. In the FA Cup, they went out in the first game they played, a 2-1 loss at Shrewsbury Town. It sounds pretty awful, but with hindsight it's worse. Why?

6. Everton had a spell in the Premier League where they won five successive matches by the same score. What was that score?

7. Similarly, they won 11 home games, seven of which were also by the same score. What was it?

8. Which American forward grabbed the two goals that beat Sunderland 2-1 at Goodison on 18 January 2003?

9. 19 October was the day the world was forced to take notice of Rooney's amazing abilities. Everyone remembers the goal he hit past David Seaman in Everton's 2-1 win. But Everton's top league goalscorer got the other one. Who was he?

10. Which central defender spent more time on the field for Everton in the Premier League that season than any other player, chalking up 35 appearances?

QUIZ No. 41

EVERTON - SEASON 2003/04

1. Well the air certainly went out of that balloon rather quickly! Everton plummeted ten places, to 17th, one spot from the drop. They were terrible on the road, winning just once in 19 tries. On whose ground?

2. Which club even managed to give Everton an own goal in each of the two league games and still won them both?

3. At least when they got on to the coach to travel to the last match of the season they could comfort themselves with the thought that no team had put five past them all season. When they got back on the coach after the game they couldn't say that anymore. Who beat them 5-1?

4. Although he didn't make double figures, Wayne Rooney was their top league goalscorer. 21 February was the only time he scored twice in a game. The goals came in a 3-3 away draw with which club?

5. Everton played in six FA Cup and League Cup ties. Who scored three times from the penalty spot in these games?

6. As usual, the League Cup came down to penalties. After putting out Stockport County and Charlton Athletic, Everton went out to the lottery from 12 yards again. The team who knocked them out won the next round by that method as well and went on to win the trophy. Who were they?

7. In the FA Cup, Everton beat Norwich City 3-1 at Goodison before losing to which London club after a replay?

8. Everton had drawn 1-1 at home and lost the replay in London 2-1. Which Everton man scored in both games?

9. Which midfielder showed the forwards how it should be done when his hat-trick was crucial in a 4-0 mauling of Leeds United at Goodison on 28 September 2003?

10. The sense of pain and betrayal was obvious on Merseyside when Wayne Rooney, their brightest hope for generations, left to join Manchester United. He scored his last Everton goal before his move on 13 April 2004 in a 1-1 away draw. On which ground?

QUIZ No. 42

EVERTON - SEASON 2004/05

1. Despite losing their talisman, Everton amazed the football world
    with a fourth-place finish and Champions League qualification.
    When was the last season they had previously finished fourth?

2. One reason for the improvement may have been that as many as ten
    players were on the pitch in 30 games or more. Which attacking
    midfielder was the only one to be on the pitch at some time in every
    game, starting 37 and coming on as a substitute in the other?

3. The biggest downer of the season concerned their two visits to north
    London. How many goals collectively did Arsenal and Spurs score
    against them?

4. On 4 January Everton beat Portsmouth 2-1 at Goodison and on
    30 April they lost 2-0 at Fulham. In the first game their opponent's goal
    was scored by someone who would later play for Everton, while in the
    later game the scorer of one of the goals that beat Everton came from
    someone who had played for them previously. Who were the two men?

5. Everton were knocked out of the two domestic cup competitions by
    Arsenal and Manchester United. Before that, they had won an FA
    Cup tie 3-1 away and a League Cup tie 2-0 at home against two sides
    beginning with a 'P'. Who were they?

6. Who was Everton's leading league goalscorer, with 11 to his name?

7. Which tough midfielder scored his last goal for Everton in a 3-2
    win over Bolton Wanderers on 4 December 2004 before moving to
    Real Madrid?

8. On 20 April Goodison enjoyed itself when Manchester United
    were beaten 1-0 and had two players sent off. Which two got their
    marching orders?

9. Who scored Everton's winner that day?

10. On 22 January, when Everton lost 1-0 at home to Charlton Athletic,
    which country scored the winner?

EVERTON - SEASON 2005/06

1. It is difficult to know what to say about this season. I suppose the charitable view to take is that 11th place was quite an achievement considering the start they made to the season. Everton won one and lost seven of their first eight games. How many goals did they score in the seven they lost?

2. The only good news until the end of October was a solitary 1-0 win at Bolton on 21 August. Who scored that oasis of a goal?

3. It wasn't surprising that it took just ten goals to be Everton's top league scorer. Who did the accolade go to?

4. Which industrious midfielder was on the pitch more than any other Everton player?

5. On which ground did the lowest number of spectators come to watch Everton in a league game, when they lost 1-0 in front of 17,169 fans?

6. Which London club did Everton beat 1-0 in the third round of the FA Cup, after drawing away 1-1 in the first game?

7. The next round gave them a more difficult London club but with home advantage. After another 1-1 draw, they were beaten 4-1 in the replay by which club?

8. One match was the extent of Everton's involvement in the League Cup, when they disappointed 25,844 inside Goodison by losing 1-0 to which northern side?

9. It wasn't just Everton's start that was problematic. In November and December they suffered three 4-0 reverses. One was at home to Bolton, while the other two were away in the Midlands. Which two clubs did the damage?

10. Their future in the Premier League might have been under threat without a good run that started on New Year's Eve with a win at Sunderland. Unbeaten in seven games, how many of those did they win?

QUIZ No. 44

EVERTON – SEASON 2006/07

1. A big improvement saw sixth place achieved. Joleon Lescott was on the field at some point in all their league matches, but two players started all 38; one was a defender and the other a midfielder. Who were they?

2. Who became Everton's top goalscorer in the Premier League, with 11 goals from his 32 games?

3. Here's a question about penalties. Which Everton player's two league goals both came from the spot, and which other Everton player got more than half of his nine league goals from that source?

4. Everton made six visits to the capital during the league season but came back to Merseyside with three points just once, on 26 August after a 2-0 win on whose ground?

5. Which Everton player scored his only league goal of the season in a 3-0 win over Newcastle United on 30 December 2006, and then would have been somewhat displeased to put through his own net when Manchester United came to Goodison on 28 April 2007?

6. The home Premier League game with Charlton Athletic on 15 April came to life in the last ten minutes when Lescott looked to have secured the points with an 81st-minute strike. However, despair reigned when Bent equalised for the visitors in the 89th minute. Joy finally erupted again in the 92nd minute when which Evertonian scored their winner?

7. You might have thought Arsenal would have dispensed enough revenge on Everton for that Rooney moment by now, but you would be wrong, as they came to Goodison and put Everton out of the League Cup. But not before Everton had beaten which two clubs from a lower division to get that far, by 2-1 away and 4-0 at home?

8. Going down 4-1 in the FA Cup was not a new experience for the Blues, but this time it was in their first match in the competition and at home into the bargain. Which Lancastrians ruined the day for the home fans?

9. Everton were masters of the away draw. Of the nine they managed on enemy territory, how many were 1-1?

10. Which Everton player was sent off in the second half of their 1-1 draw at Newcastle United on 24 September 2006?

QUIZ No. 45

EVERTON - SEASON 2007/08

1. A solid season again, with a fifth-place finish. The highlight of the league season came on 24 November 2007 when the Goodison fans were treated to a great 7-1 win over which club?

2. Two of the goals that day were scored by their top goalscorer in both the league and the League Cup, with 17 in those two competitions. Who was he?

3. Everton's Player of the Year was the only man to start all 38 Premier League games. Who was he?

4. Who put through his own net at Wigan when Everton won 2-1 in January, and then early in the next month got a Goodison winner against Reading?

5. The season's bad news was that yet again Everton couldn't do a thing in the FA Cup. Drawn at home in the third round, the game was delayed by half an hour because of a fire outside the ground. What the fans would have given for some fire from the home team inside the ground. The referee was Uriah Rennie, so perhaps he put the fire out. I've seen those diagrams on the adverts for indigestion and it always works! Who did Everton lose to 1-0?

6. Everton fared much better in the League Cup, reaching the semi-final stage. To get to that point, they won 3-0 in Yorkshire, 1-0 after extra time in Bedfordshire and 2-1 in London. Which three teams bit the dust?

7. Everton would have met Spurs in the final of that competition if they hadn't lost that semi-final 3-1 over the two legs to a side who often rained on their parade. Who were they?

8. Everton's home record was identical to their record for the previous season. What was the win, lose and draw breakdown in each of those seasons at Goodison over those 19 games?

9. Yakubu scored a second-half hat-trick in a 3-0 home win over which London club on 8 December 2007?

10. Which Arsenal player was sent off at Goodison on 29 December 2007, missing the last 16 minutes of a game they won 4-1, and then got the winner in the return?

QUIZ No. 46

EVERTON - SEASON 2008/09

1. Fifth again and the bonus of a visit to Wembley for the FA Cup final, although it didn't end well. Everton accumulated more points away from Goodison than at that ground. The last time that happened was before I was born and I'm no spring chicken! In what season was it?

2. In their run to the FA Cup final they scored eight goals. What was unusual about them?

3. After making hard work of getting past Macclesfield, the omens weren't good when they were drawn at Anfield in the fourth round. However, they brought Liverpool back to Goodison and in a very tense atmosphere beat them after extra time. Which Liverpool player received a red card in that game?

4. After Aston Villa and Middlesbrough had been beaten 3-1 and 2-1 at Goodison, Manchester United awaited the Toffees in the semi-final. Even extra time failed to produce a goal, before Everton came good in the penalty shoot-out. It didn't look so good when they went first and missed, but eventually they prevailed 4-2. Who missed that first kick and who scored the deciding goal from the spot?

5. The Premier League game with the most goals came in a 3-3 draw at Villa Park on 12 April 2009. The scorer of Villa's equaliser from the penalty spot later became an Evertonian. Who was he?

6. Who grabbed an equaliser in the league at Anfield on 19 January, three minutes from the end, to cancel out Steven Gerrard's earlier goal?

7. Everton's participation in the League Cup lasted one trip of about 30 miles in a north-easterly direction when they lost 1-0 to which club?

8. When Everton lost at Arsenal in the Premier League on 18 October, which player who would later join Everton made the game safe for the home side in the last minute by making it 3-1?

9. Which two players, one from Chelsea and the other from Newcastle United, were sent off against Everton during the Premier League season?

10. When Everton beat Bolton Wanderers 3-0 on 7 February at Goodison, two players scored from the penalty spot for them. Who were they?

QUIZ No. 47

EVERTON - SEASON 2009/10

1. Everton experienced too many injuries to be competitive before the new year but made great strides in the second half of the season to eventually finish eighth. They got a terrible shock on the opening day at Goodison when Arsenal, not for the first time, took them to the cleaners by what score?

2. After that shock to the system it was important to bounce back, but they lost their next match 1-0 at Burnley when their leading-goalscorer-to-be missed a penalty. Who was he?

3. After opening wins in both domestic cup competitions, against Carlisle United in the FA Cup and Hull City in the League Cup, they were dumped out of both by teams from the second city and the capital city. Who were the two teams?

4. Who, for the second year running, didn't miss a single Premier League game?

5. The season's biggest Premier League victory was by 5-1 at Goodison on 7 March 2010 against a team that would be relegated at the season's end. Who were they?

6. Which Everton player got a hat-trick in the game?

7. Who scored from the penalty spot four minutes into added time to give Everton a 2-1 win against the Lancastrian side that were his previous club on 30 August 2009 at Goodison?

8. On 27 January 2010, when Everton won 2-0 at home to Sunderland, one of their scorers was a new boy from the USA who shared a surname with a popular Everton player last seen at Goodison in 1958. Who was the goalscorer?

9. On 24 March David Moyes was shown a red card by the referee in an away game that Everton won 2-0. It came in the 91st minute and the opposing manager also received one. Who was he?

CALL YOURSELF A TOFFEES FAN?

10. This guy made an interesting impact at the start of his time with the Toffees. On 17 October 2009 he scored in a 1-1 Goodison draw with Wolves, and then two weeks later on the same ground he scored again in another 1-1 draw, this time against Aston Villa. Not long after that, he got sent off. Quite a start! Who was he, and a bonus point if you spell it correctly?

QUIZ No. 48

EVERTON - SEASON 2010/11

1. Everton finished seventh in the Premier League and on the way won 5-3 at Goodison against Lancastrian rivals with an Everton player claiming four of the five. Who did they beat and who got the four-timer?

2. The most dramatic finish to a game was also at Goodison, when a seemingly unassailable 3-1 lead for Manchester United disappeared in added time when which two Everton players came up trumps with the goals to earn the home side a 3-3 draw?

3. Everton won their first match in the FA Cup against Scunthorpe United and their first match in the League Cup against Huddersfield Town by the same score. What was it?

4. In the next round of the FA Cup, they beat one London side 4-3 on penalties, while in the next round of the League Cup they went out to another London club 4-3 on penalties. Which two clubs were involved?

5. Everton were the only club to perform a league double over them when they won 2-1 home and away. Who were they?

6. He wasn't Everton's top goalscorer but he did come up with some very useful late goals. In November his goal four minutes into added time saved Everton a home point against Bolton, and in the following month he repeated the trick four minutes from the end at Stamford Bridge, both games ending 1-1. Who was he?

7. If he wasn't Everton's leading league goalscorer, who was?

8. Everton were very generous on their travels with own goals, tossing them about like confetti! At one point in the season, they gave one away in three successive away games, at Manchester City, Stoke City and West Ham United. Which two players were generous to a fault?

9. Which club from a lower division knocked Everton out of the FA Cup 1-0 in the fifth round at Goodison after the Toffees had got over one tough hurdle and had the fans dreaming of Wembley again?

10. Two Everton players received red cards at Goodison during the season, in games against Bolton Wanderers and West Bromwich Albion. Who were the two players?

QUIZ No. 49

EVERTON - SEASON 2011/12

1. Everton finished seventh again in the Premier League but had to be thankful for the nine goals that were enough to make which player their top scorer, despite not arriving from Glasgow Rangers until January?

2. Which Everton player was picked in the PFA Team of the Year?

3. The most exciting ten minutes of the season came with the Blues trailing 4-2 at Old Trafford on 22 April 2012. Which two players scored for Everton to draw the game at 4-4 and effectively move the Premier League trophy from one part of Manchester to another?

4. Everton had a great run to the FA Cup semi-final, beating Fulham, Blackpool and Sunderland before the old enemy intervened at Wembley. Which non-league side gave them a good game before going down 2-0 at Goodison in the third round?

5. In the League Cup, between knocking out Sheffield United and being themselves knocked out by Chelsea, they beat West Brom 2-1 after extra time at Goodison. Who got their 103rd-minute winner?

6. Not counting the FA Cup semi-final against Liverpool, what was unusual about Everton's games in both domestic cup competitions?

7. Whose first goal for Everton, at Goodison on 31 January 2012, gave them a 1-0 win that would have pleased the team he came from almost as much as the team he scored it for?

8. One of the goals that helped Spurs beat Everton 2-0 at White Hart Lane on 11 January 2012 was scored by someone who later joined the Merseysiders. Who was he?

9. In five days before Christmas, between 17 and 21 December, Everton played two home games. They were saved late on when drawing 1-1 with Norwich City in the first of them, and then won the second against Swansea City 1-0. The same man dug them out of trouble, with a goal in the first game and then scored the winner in the second. Who was he?

10. After their traditional slow start to the campaign, Everton won at Goodison for the first time on 17 September 2011, beating Wigan Athletic 3-1. Which two newcomers won it for them by scoring in the last ten minutes?

QUIZ No. 50

EVERTON – SEASON 2012/13

1. Everton achieved a sixth-place finish after a great start to the season saw a Fellaini goal give them a 1-0 opening day win over which club at Goodison Park?

2. They only lost one league game on their own ground all season. It came against a club from the capital. Which one?

3. Which Everton player started every league game and was picked for the PFA Team of the Year?

4. Which player scored home and away for Wigan against Everton and attracted enough attention in doing so to eventually end up at Goodison?

5. What was unusual about Everton's 1-1 draw at Loftus Road against QPR on 21 October 2012?

6. Who, with 11 goals, was the club's top scorer in the Premier League?

7. In the League Cup Everton played two teams beginning with 'L', beating the first of them 5-0 and then going out of the competition to the second by 2-1. Who were the two teams?

8. On 9 December 2012 Everton trailed 1-0 to Spurs at home going into added time. Three minutes later they had won the game 2-1. Which two players landed the blows that turned the game on its head?

9. In the return at White Hart Lane on 7 April 2013 there was also late drama when Spurs scored in the 87th minute to make it 2-2. The scorer later joined the Toffees. Who was he?

10. The FA Cup looked promising when Everton were drawn at home to Wigan Athletic after accounting for Cheltenham Town, Bolton Wanderers and Oldham Athletic. It was a big let down when they lost 3-0. In the Bolton tie, whose 91st-minute goal decided it in Everton's favour 2-1?

QUIZ No. 51

EVERTON - SEASON 2013/14

1. Under new man Roberto Martinez, Everton finished fifth and broke Premier League club records by recording seven straight wins and what else?

2. Whose 15 Premier League goals won him the accolade of Everton's top scorer?

3. Which two London clubs did Everton meet in domestic cup competition, beating the first of them 4-0 at Goodison in the third round of the FA Cup, while losing to the other 2-1 away from home in the League Cup?

4. Which Everton defender made the PFA Team of the Year?

5. Which club did Everton eject from both the FA Cup and the League Cup during the season, winning 4-0 away in the former but struggling to get the job done in the latter, winning 2-1 after extra time at Goodison?

6. What did Tim Howard, Bryan Oviedo, Seamus Coleman and Antolin Alcaraz all do during the season?

7. Lukaku didn't see his header go into the net to give Everton a 3-2 away win on 21 September 2013 because he was knocked out in the process. He also got the only goal of the game at Goodison Park in the return game. Who did Everton beat in those two games?

8. David Moyes was probably not best pleased that Everton waited until he was the Manchester United manager before they decided to win there! They did so by 1-0 on 4 December 2013 through whose goal?

9. It would have been even more galling for him when they beat Manchester United again, by 2-0, on 20 April 2014 at Goodison Park. Why?

10. Everton recorded one of their rare wins against Arsenal on 6 April 2014 by 3-0 at Goodison, although Arsenal still managed to knock them out of the FA Cup at the quarter-final stage. In that league game, whose own goal to make it 3-0 put the icing on the cake?

QUIZ No. 52

EVERTON - SEASON 2014/15

1. Everton's 11th-place finish was their worst for nine years and the Thursday nights in the Europa League didn't help their cause much. At least they were involved in the highest scoring Premier League game of the season, but there was a sting in that tail as Chelsea came to Goodison and won 6-3. Which ex-Chelsea player got one of Everton's goals against his old club?

2. Who scored Everton's first goal of the season after 20 minutes of the opening day of the Premier League at Leicester in a match that ended up a 2-2 draw?

3. On 21 September Crystal Palace came to Goodison and ran out 3-2 winners. One of their goals was scored by a player who eventually left them to join Everton. Who was he?

4. Manchester United were proving less of a problem for Everton these days and they beat them 3-0 at Goodison on 26 April 2015. Who scored his first goal for the Toffees in this game?

5. In the FA Cup Lukaku's added-time goal at Goodison took Everton to West Ham for a replay that ended 2-2 after extra time. The penalty shoot-out went on so long some people may have missed the last bus home, but Everton came out on the wrong side of the 9-8 scoreline. Whose miss finally ended the tie?

6. Their participation in the League Cup was even shorter, lasting one trip to Wales, where Swansea beat them 3-0. One of their goals was scored by a future Everton player. Who was he?

7. Who was Everton's top goalscorer in both the Premier League and the FA Cup?

8. Which Everton defender missed just one of their 38 Premier League games?

9. In the two league games with Swansea City, which both ended in draws, one of the opposition's players was in the news by getting sent off at Goodison and scoring from the spot at the Liberty Stadium. Who was he?

10. On the first day of 2015 Everton lost 2-0 at Hull City, where one of the home side's goals came from an ex-Everton man. Who was he?

QUIZ No. 53

EVERTON - SEASON 2015/16

1. Two excellent cup runs with nothing to show at the end of them and an 11th-place finish, again, with the lowest points total on home soil since the change to three points for a win in 1981. Roberto Martinez paid the price after a 3-0 away defeat on 11 May 2016 against which club?

2. The home game against that club had been an altogether different affair on the first day of November. The visitors scored twice. How many did Everton get?

3. Who was the only Everton man to be on the pitch in every Premier League game?

4. Romelu Lukaku made a clean sweep of the top goalscorer stakes in the Premier League and both domestic cup competitions, becoming the first Everton player to score 25 times in a season since which man?

5. Who scored all three Everton goals when they beat Chelsea 3-1 at Goodison Park on 12 September 2015?

6. Everton thought they had grabbed a very late winner when Ross Barkley scored to put them 3-2 up away from home in the 95th minute on 28 November 2015. But the home side had other ideas and made it 3-3 in the 98th minute. Who were they?

7. When Manchester United visited Goodison on 17 October 2015 and won 3-0, one of their goals was scored by an ex-Evertonian and another was scored by someone who would shortly become one. Who were the two players?

8. Who scored his first goal for the Toffees in a 1-0 Boxing Day win at Newcastle United three minutes into added time?

9. In the FA Cup quarter-final at Goodison that ended with a 2-0 win over Chelsea on 12 March 2016, one player from each side received a red card. Who were the two players?

10. Which player made his 414th and final Everton appearance in the 3-0 win over Norwich City on the last day of the season at Goodison on 15 May 2016?

QUIZ No. 54

EVERTON - SEASON 2016/17

1. Everton improved into seventh place in the Premier League after gaining the most points at home since which season?

2. The season was a triumph for Lukaku, who was on the pitch for all but one league game, made the PFA Team of the Year and on 4 February 2017 got four goals in a game at Goodison Park. Who did Everton beat and by what score?

3. That wasn't all. He became the first man since Dixie Dean in the 1930s to score in how many successive home games?

4. Who was Everton's top scorer in the League Cup, despite not scoring at all in the Premier League?

5. After beating Yeovil Town 4-0 in that competition, Everton were knocked out in the next round 2-0 at home to Norwich City. One of the goals was scored by an ex-Evertonian. Who?

6. Who celebrated his 600th Premier League game with one of the goals with which Everton beat Middlesbrough 3-1 at Goodison on 17 September 2016?

7. A major disappointment was failing to progress past the first hurdle in the FA Cup. Which Midlands club, despite falling behind to a Lukaku goal just after the hour mark, came back to win 2-1?

8. Two goalkeepers gave Everton a helping hand during the season with own goals. The first came in a 1-0 win over Stoke City at Goodison in August, with the second following in December at Hull City in a 2-2 draw. Who were the two goalkeepers?

9. Possibly the performance of the season came at Goodison Park on 15 January 2017, when Manchester City were sent packing 4-0. The icing on the cake was the last goal of the game in the 93rd minute, which constituted the first of his Everton career for which man?

10. Although Everton lost the Anfield Merseyside derby 3-1, their goal was scored by a defender who was opening his account for the club. Who was he?

EVERTON - SEASON 2017/18

1. Everton were in the relegation places on 22 October 2017, after two wins from their opening nine games. On that day, which club beat Everton 5-2 at Goodison and which manager's job was over?

2. After David Unsworth had steadied the ship for five games, Sam Allardyce, 'Messes Cleared Up incorporated', was appointed to deal with the latest one. He won his first game in charge 2-0 at Goodison against which club?

3. At the end of the season he was surplus to requirements after having done what he was appointed for, his brand of football not sexy enough, whatever that means! What position were Everton in when he was shown the door?

4. There were mixed feelings in the blue half of the city about the return of Wayne Rooney. He didn't do his cause any harm by scoring in the first two games of the season, a 1-0 home win and a 1-1 away draw. Who were the opponents?

5. Whose two goals were vital when Everton won 2-1 against Bournemouth at Goodison on 23 September 2017?

6. Everton staged a great rally after trailing 2-0 at home to Watford on Bonfire Night, the fireworks coming in the final third of the game when Niasse got one back and Calvert-Lewin equalised. Who got their 91st-minute winner?

7. The scorer of the first Watford goal that day later became an Evertonian. Who was he?

8. On 29 November 2017 the Goodison crowd were treated to the Rooney show when his hat-trick included a breath-taking goal. It was bittersweet for true blues because it gave them a glimpse of what they might have had over the previous 14 years or so. Which club were beaten 4-0 on the day?

9.   Everton's activity in the January transfer window paid dividends on the last day of that month when who scored both goals in their 2-1 win over Leicester City at Goodison?

10. Not to be outdone, another of their buys came good with the two goals by which they won 2-1 at Stoke City on 17 March 2018. Who was he?

QUIZ No. 56

EVERTON - SEASON 2018/19

1. Everton finished eighth in Marco Silva's first season as manager and the jury was still out. Which Everton player was sent off in Silva's first match in charge, a 2-2 draw at Wolves on the season's opening day?

2. The honour of being leading Everton goalscorer in the Premier League was shared between two players, who both found the net 13 times. Who were they?

3. It was typical of Everton to lose 6-2 at home one week and then win 5-1 away the next! That's exactly what they did over four days in December 2018. Which two clubs were involved?

4. In the FA Cup, they beat Lincoln City 2-1 in the third round before a visit to the capital in the next round. It was quite a battle, and the match was difficult as well! Who knocked them out 3-2?

5. In the League Cup, who got two of the three goals Everton scored at Goodison when beating Rotherham 3-1?

6. They went out on penalties in the next round after finishing 1-1 against Southampton on Merseyside. Who was the unlucky man that missed the last penalty?

7. Which defender saved the game for Everton when he made it 2-2 six minutes into added-on time against Watford at Goodison on 10 December 2018?

8. Who had a nice Christmas bonus in the shape of his first Premier League goal for the club when it took him just two minutes to give Everton the lead on Boxing Day at Turf Moor?

9. Which central defender scored for Everton in their 2-0 win over Bournemouth at Goodison Park in the Premier League on 13 January 2019?

10. Who was the only player to start all 38 Premier League games for Everton?

QUIZ No. 57

EVERTON - SEASON 2019/20

1. Everton were fifth from bottom when it became clear that Marco
    Silva was no miracle worker. He had the plug pulled on him after a
    5-2 defeat against which club? As if you didn't know!

2. Duncan Ferguson's enthusiasm gave the club some momentum
    before the appointment of a manager with some real pedigree in
    Carlo Ancelotti. Where did they finish in the Premier League by the
    end of the craziest season ever?

3. For the second season running, the goalscoring plaudits were shared
    by two men who, also like the previous year, each scored 13 Premier
    League goals. Who were they this time?

4. The old enemy knocked Everton out of the FA Cup, but they had a
    good run in the League Cup. After a 4-2 win at Lincoln City, they
    were drawn at Sheffield Wednesday and won that one 2-0. Their
    first home tie brought Watford to Goodison, where they were beaten
    2-0. Who scored his first goal for the club in that game?

5. Unfortunately, in the next round it was that old bugbear, the
    penalty shoot-out, that came back to bite them again at Goodison.
    Leighton Baines scored with his 92nd-minute penalty to make it 2-2
    and get Everton into the lottery, but he then missed his penalty in
    the shoot-out. Which club went into the next round?

6. February's first day proved to be a good one for an Everton defender.
    If you get one goal, you are very pleased with yourself. He got two
    within three minutes of each other in Everton's 3-2 win at Watford.
    Who was he?

7. The season was effectively divided in two by the Covid nightmare.
    On 1 March Everton played what turned out to be their last game at
    Goodison for over three and a half months. It finished in a 1-1 draw.
    Who were they playing?

8. Which Everton player put through his own net when Spurs beat
    them 1-0 in London on 6 July 2020?

9. The same player gave them a 1-0 away win on 24 June 2020, with what was their first goal since the first day of March. Which club was it against?

10. It's not every day that a player brings down the curtain on his career in July, but this is what happened to Leighton Baines after over 400 appearances for Everton. The occasion proved a damp squib as Everton contrived to lose the game 3-1. To which club?

QUIZ No. 58

EVERTON - SEASON 2020/21

1. Everton set off like a whirlwind at the start of the season, winning their first four matches and scoring nine times in their first two at Goodison. Heady times, indeed! Which two clubs conceded those nine goals?

2. The other two victories came in visits to London, where they won 1-0 on the opening day and 2-1 a fortnight later. Who were the beaten clubs and which Everton player hit the ground running by scoring in all the first five games of the season?

3. A 2-2 draw with Liverpool on 17 October ended the winning run, and their first defeat came the following week at Southampton. An Everton player received a red card in each of those games. Which two players were sent off?

4. Two Everton defenders came to the fore at the other end of the pitch by scoring winning goals for the club. The first came in a home game with Arsenal, which they won 2-1 in December, and the second early in the new year, when they won by the same score at Wolves. Which two players scored those goals?

5. It was great to win at Anfield on 20 February by 2-0, but such a shame that when that long-awaited moment arrived, no Everton fan could be there to see it. Which two players scored the vital goals?

6. Everton reached the quarter-final of each domestic cup competition before going out at home to both Manchester clubs by the same score of 2-0 when hopes were high that they would progress to the semis. In the League Cup's previous round, they had won 4-1 with a Calvert-Lewin hat-trick. Who did they beat and which other club during the season did Calvert-Lewin score a hat-trick against?

7. Which Everton player scored winning goals in the Premier League at home to Southampton and Wolves and away to Crystal Palace and West Brom?

8.   Before scoring five times at Fleetwood in the League Cup, Everton had knocked out Salford City 3-0 at Goodison in the previous round. If you add one letter to the scorer of one of their goals you get the man who scored another of them. Who are the two players?

9.   After accounting for Rotherham United and Sheffield Wednesday at the first two hurdles in the FA Cup, the fifth round produced a real thriller at Goodison when Everton got through 5-4 after extra time. Who were their opponents?

10. Who came up with Everton's winner in that extra-time period?

QUIZ No. 59

EVERY LITTLE HELPS (OWN GOALS)

1. Who put through his own net to score for Everton in a 2-2 draw with Leicester City at Goodison on 22 February 2015?

2. Who repeated the trick while playing for Swansea at Goodison on 24 January 2016? It didn't matter in the end as the away side won 2-1.

3. Chelsea and Everton drew 3-3 at Stamford Bridge on 16 January 2016. Which Chelsea player scored at both ends?

4. Whose own goal in the FA Cup semi-final while playing for Manchester United wasn't enough to get Everton into the final in the 2015/16 season?

5. When Everton drew 1-1 at Stoke City on 1 February 2017, which Stoke player scored for the visitors?

6. This next man has scored more than some Everton players! On 15 April 2017 he started the ball rolling with one of Everton's goals in their 3-1 win over Burnley at Goodison and then, on 3 May 2019 on the same ground, got one of Everton's two in their 2-0 win over the same club. Who is he?

7. Which Arsenal player scored Everton's goal when they lost 3-1 away to the Gunners on 21 May 2017?

8. Everton drew 1-1 at Swansea City on 14 April 2018. Which player on the home side scored for the visitors?

9. On 26 October 2019, which Brighton player scored one of Everton's goals on the south coast when the visitors went down 3-2?

10. Which member of the opposition scored Everton's goal in a 1-1 draw at Old Trafford on 15 December 2019?

QUIZ No. 60

THE FA CUP FINALS OF
1893, 1897, 1906, 1907 AND 1933

1. Everton were favourites when they reached their first FA Cup final in 1893 but went down 1-0 to which club?

2. Which club, by beating Everton 3-2 in the 1897 final, completed the league and cup double that season?

3. Everton finally got the job done in 1906, when for the first time they kept a clean sheet in the final, which meant that their solitary goal was enough to take the prize against which club?

4. Their winning goal was scored by someone who shares a surname with an Everton player who was in the side that contested an FA Cup final 60 years later. What was that surname?

5. The following season, they made a good fist of defending the trophy but were beaten in the final 2-1 by which Yorkshire club?

6. Everton's goalscorer that day had a surname that would appear again as a goalscorer for Everton in an FA Cup final over three quarters of a century later. What was that surname?

7. In the 1933 final, Everton had a resounding 3-0 win over which club?

8. What innovation concerning players' shirts was in evidence for the first time at that final?

9. No player appeared in all of Everton's first three FA Cup finals of 1893, 1897 and 1906. True or false?

10. The crowd at the 1933 FA Cup final was more than double that at their first final in 1893. True or false?

QUIZ No. 61

THE FA CUP FINALS OF 1966, 1968, 1984 AND 1985

1. 1966 provided the first occasion where Everton were meeting a side they had played in an earlier final. Who did they play in 1966 and what was the score?

2. That final produced a great fightback by the Blues and one player wrote himself firmly into their history, despite playing just 11 league games for the club, when he grabbed two goals. Who was he?

3. Which surname could be found in the line-ups of both clubs?

4. Everton lost the 1968 final in extra time to which club?

5. What colours did Everton play in that day?

6. What was unique to FA Cup finals about the first three names on Everton's team sheet for the 1968 final?

7. Which club did Everton beat 2-0 in the 1984 final and which player scored their second goal?

8. In the 1985 final against Manchester United, Kevin Moran was sent off for a tackle that sent which Everton player catapulting through the air?

9. Which member of the Manchester United team that won the cup that day had been signed from Everton?

10. Which man who was playing in his first FA Cup final that day for Everton went on to play in three more finals without ever gaining a winner's medal?

QUIZ No. 62

THE FA CUP FINALS OF 1986, 1989, 1995 AND 2009

1. Who put Everton ahead against Liverpool in the 1986 final before the roof fell in?

2. If you take one Everton player from that day and add just one letter to his surname, you produce another Everton man who also played in that final. Who are the two players?

3. Unfortunately, Everton also lost to Liverpool in the 1989 final, by 3-2 after extra time. Which five Everton players started in both matches?

4. In that 1989 final, which Everton player scored their two goals and what was unique about his contribution?

5. Which three members of the Liverpool team in that 1989 final have also played for Everton at some time during their career?

6. Everton inflicted some revenge on Manchester United by beating them in the 1995 final ten years after losing to them by the same 1-0 scoreline. Who scored Everton's goal?

7. Which Everton player received the Man of the Match award in that 1995 final?

8. Everton made a great start to the 2009 final when which player put them into an early lead against Chelsea?

9. It wasn't just an early goal. It was the fastest in a first-class game at Wembley. What was it timed at?

10. Sadly, Everton went on to lose that final by 2-1. Which two Everton players had previously played in an FA Cup final?

QUIZ No. 63

FA CUP SEMI-FINALS

1. Up to 2020 Everton have contested 26 FA Cup semi-finals. Have they won more than half or lost more than half?

2. Which London club have Everton met the most times in an FA Cup semi-final?

3. Who are the only club that Everton have met two years running in an FA Cup semi-final? It happened in 1897 and 1898.

4. Which club have Everton met the most times in an FA Cup semi-final?

5. The 2009 semi-final was the only one Everton have played in where the outcome was decided by penalties. Who were they playing?

6. Between 1984 and 2009 Everton had a winning run where FA Cup semi-finals were concerned. How many did they win?

7. Who are the most southerly club that Everton have played in an FA Cup semi-final?

8. Which three Yorkshire clubs have Everton played against in an FA Cup semi-final, the first in 1910, the second in 1968 and the third in 1986?

9. Who are the only two post-war Everton players to score more than once in an FA Cup semi-final?

10. Who are the only two clubs that have appeared in more FA Cup semi-finals than Everton?

GOALKEEPERS

1. He guarded Everton's net in 124 league games between 1972 and 1978, as well as all three matches against Aston Villa in the 1977 League Cup final. He had joined from Huddersfield and left for Luton. Who was he?

2. In spite of being the man who conceded the most goals in one game for the Toffees, he was a great servant to the club, playing 211 league games in a career that spanned three decades. He finally moved on to Wrexham in 1963, where I saw him have a game in a 0-0 draw at Chesterfield that was just about the greatest I've seen from any goalkeeper. Who was he?

3. It was Everton moving for this Blackpool goalkeeper in 1962 that prompted the move away from Goodison by the answer to the previous question. The new boy went on to play 335 league matches for Everton before a move in 1975 to Tranmere Rovers. Who was he?

4. While struggling at times to hold down a place in the side, this 1980s Everton goalkeeper played for them in an FA Cup final and ended up with league title medals at both Everton and Blackburn Rovers. Who was he?

5. This popular goalkeeper turned out in the league 201 times for Everton and won 17 caps for the Republic of Ireland before he joined Stoke City in 1960. Who was he?

6. It seems almost impossible to believe that a footballer's career could extend over four decades, but this great goalkeeper's did. He made 463 league appearances between 1929 and 1953, and, but for the war, that figure may well have been in the 700s. Who was he?

7. Capped 52 times for Wales, this goalkeeper came from Swansea and left for Wrexham, but not before playing 82 games for Everton between 1970 and 1977. His death was announced in early 2021 and

was the subject of a tribute before Everton's FA Cup tie with Spurs at Goodison. Who was he?

8. Which goalkeeper in this century played just once for the club and is one of only two goalkeepers in English football to have two successive 'A's' in his name? For a bonus point, who is the other one?

9. Which Everton goalkeeper came through the juniors and made 85 league appearances between 1961 and 1971, when he was transferred to Watford?

10. Which Belfast-born goalkeeper was the first to win an FA Cup winner's medal when Everton won the trophy for the first time in 1906? Between 1904 and 1912 he played in 251 league games for the club.

QUIZ No. 65

GOODISON PARK - PART 1

1. In which area of Liverpool is Goodison Park situated?

2. Which Midlands club were the first to play Everton at Goodison Park on 3 September 1892 in a game that ended in a 2-2 draw?

3. Which Everton player scored their first league and cup goal on the ground?

4. Their first win on their new ground came on 24 September 1892 in a resounding 6-0 hammering of Newton Heath. Who did that club eventually become?

5. It was hardly surprising that it was that season's champions that lowered Everton's colours on the ground for the first time when they won there 4-1 on 8 October 1892. Who were they?

6. Goodison Park was widely used for England internationals down the years, the first coming on 6 April 1895 when England beat which country 3-0?

7. Starting with that 1895 international, when was the next decade that Goodison Park failed to be chosen to host an international?

8. When England beat Ireland on the ground on 22 October 1928 it was a special occasion because an Everton player scored one of their goals in a 2-1 win. Who?

9. In the 1895/96 season a scandal engulfed Goodison Park that led to plain-clothes police operating in the ground on a match day and ended with 15 arrests. What offence were they charged with?

10. Which two countries contested a World Cup semi-final at Goodison Park in 1966?

QUIZ No. 66

GOODISON PARK - PART 2

1. Everton moved from Anfield to Goodison Park in 1892 after a row over an intended rent increase by the owner of the ground. Who was he?

2. Everton won the rights to that name through an FA tribunal and paid £8,090 for the site across Stanley Park that eventually became Goodison Park. What was its name when they acquired it?

3. After significant investment, Goodison Park became one of the foremost grounds in the country and within two years was chosen to stage the 1894 FA Cup final, in which Bolton Wanderers were beaten 4-1 by a Midlands club whose success in that final has proved to be its only one. Who won it that day?

4. The only other time Goodison was used as a venue for an FA Cup final came before World War One, when it hosted the replay between Newcastle United and Barnsley. In what year?

5. Which Midlands club were Everton's first FA Cup opponents on the ground when they visited on 21 January 1893 and went back south defeated 4-1?

6. Which country played all three of its group-stage matches at Goodison Park in the 1966 World Cup?

7. You wouldn't fit them all in today but Goodison's record attendance is 78,299 and was set against Liverpool on 18 September, when the sides drew 1-1, in which year?

8. Two innovations occurred at Goodison Park closely together in 1957 and 1958, in the second of which they were leading the way for the other clubs. What were those two innovations?

9. Goodison Park was treated to an amazing World Cup quarter-final in 1966, when Portugal came back from 3-0 down to defeat North Korea 5-3. Several sources say it was South Korea. Don't believe them. Which famous player scored four goals in that game?

10. Very sadly it looks as though Goodison Park won't be around for much longer. In its close-on 120 seasons of hosting league football, why is 1962/63 unique?

QUIZ No. 67

IF THE CAP FITS - PART 1

All the answers are players who have been capped post-war for England while at Everton.

1. In this period Everton have had five players who were capped for England just once while at the club. Two of them were capped in the 1960s, one in the 1970s, one in the 1990s and the other in 2001. Can you name them?

2. Which man nosed ahead of all five by gaining two England caps in 2013?

3. Two defenders with names beginning with 'L' both got 26 caps in their overall careers. Who were they?

4. Who, with 40 caps between 2008 and 2017, was Everton's most capped England player this century until Jordan Pickford overtook him?

5. Who is the only man to be capped post-war for England with both Liverpool and Everton?

6. Which Everton player gained 30 caps between 2010 and 2015?

7. Which full-back and centre-forward, both signed from Blackburn Rovers, played for England between 1964 and 1970?

8. Which Everton signing from Burnley played five times in midfield for England in the mid-1970s?

9. Which Everton player scored five times for England in 12 outings between 1978 and 1979?

10. These can be found in peaches, a garden and a recording studio, but also played for England this century while at Everton. Who is he?

QUIZ No. 68

IF THE CAP FITS - PART 2

All the answers are players who have been capped post-war by either Scotland, Wales, Northern Ireland or the Republic of Ireland.

1. Which goalkeeper, capped in the late 1970s, is Everton's only Scottish international in that position in the post-war era?

2. Which Everton defender was capped 17 times with the Republic of Ireland, the first of which came in 1961 when he had already been at Goodison nine years?

3. James Oster, Pat Van den Hauwe and that great centre-half Tommy Jones all received the same number of Welsh caps. How many?

4. His father scored a legendary goal for Scotland and after signing for Everton in 1999 he went on to amass a total of 26 caps for his country. Who was he?

5. Which player, who was capped for the Republic of Ireland with West Brom, Sunderland, Wigan and Hull, as well as Everton, went on to gain over 100 caps?

6. Two players whose names begin with the same letter won caps with Everton that helped towards their final totals, which, for both of them, were exactly 50. They were both creative midfielders whose careers were played out almost entirely in the 1970s, one of them winning his caps for Scotland, while the other won his with Northern Ireland. Who are the two players?

7. A goalkeeper from the 1970s and a midfielder from the first decade of this century share playing for Everton, Welsh caps and their surname. Who are the two players?

8. These two Scottish internationals share a surname. One received his 31 caps between 1951 and 1965 while the other got his 58th and last while at Everton in the year 2000. What is that surname?

9. Two great Welshmen who played for Everton, Gary Speed and Ashley Williams, together played 171 times for their country. There's only one cap between them. Who, with 86, has the edge?

10. Two Everton Scottish internationals this century, one with a total of 46 caps and the other with more than 50, have the same surname apart from just one letter. Who are the two players?

QUIZ No. 69

MANAGERS - PART 1

1. Which post-war Everton manager played as a goalkeeper during his football career?

2. Who is the only man to have three spells managing Everton?

3. Who is the only man to manage Everton in the 20th and 21st centuries?

4. Who is the only Everton manager to score the winning goal in a European Cup final?

5. Who are the only two Everton managers to have taken a team to success in the Champions League?

6. Who is the only 20th-century Everton manager to have captained a team to win the FA Cup?

7. Everton manager Billy Bingham played in an FA Cup final and scored the semi-final-replay winner that got his team to Wembley. Who were they?

8. What links Everton managers Johnny Carey, Gordon Lee, Howard Kendall and Sam Allardyce?

9. Who managed Everton in two different centuries, being at the club between 1889 and 1901?

10. Which post-war Everton manager played for Aston Villa in the first League Cup final of 1961?

MANAGERS - PART 2

1. No manager has won the FA Cup more than once with Everton. True or false?

2. Which two clubs that share the same colours had Marco Silva managed before he came to Everton?

3. Which member of Everton's FA Cup-winning side of 1933 later managed the club?

4. Which four ex-Everton players have taken on the role of caretaker manager?

5. Which two post-war Everton managers have won the FA Cup with other clubs?

6. Who is the only man to lead Everton to the titles of the Second Division and First Division in successive seasons?

7. Who was Everton's manager when they won the FA Cup for the first time in 1906?

8. Which Everton manager received one cap for England during his playing career?

9. Which club besides Everton links Howard Kendall and David Moyes?

10. Who is the only Everton manager to win a European competition with the club?

QUIZ No. 71

MULTIPLE CHOICE

1. Which one of these clubs has won the FA Cup the same number of times as Everton?
   A) West Brom B) Bolton Wanderers C) Wolves D) Sheffield United

2. Who is the only Everton goalkeeper to score for them in the Premier League?
   A) Paul Gerrard B) Neville Southall C) Tim Howard
   D) Jordan Pickford

3. Which one of these Everton players won the most England caps over their entire career?
   A) Phil Jagielka B) Joleon Lescott C) Gary Stevens D) Trevor Steven

4. Who were the last club to play against Everton in the Charity/Community Shield?
   A) Blackburn Rovers B) Chelsea C) Liverpool D) Coventry City

5. Which one of these teams has appeared in the same number of FA Cup finals as Everton?
   A) Chelsea B) Liverpool C) Aston Villa D) Newcastle United

6. Who is the only goalkeeper to score against Everton in the Premier League?
   A) David James B) Peter Schmeichel C) Brad Friedel
   D) Paul Robinson

7. Who scored the most League Cup goals for Everton from the competition's inception in 1960 to the end of the century?
   A) Tony Cottee B) Graeme Sharp C) Bob Latchford
   D) Adrian Heath

8. Which player, because of vagaries concerning the dates of ties, ended up scoring for Everton in both January and December of 1999, the same calendar year but in two different FA Cup seasons?
   A) Duncan Ferguson B) Nicky Barmby C) David Unsworth
   D) Francis Jeffers

9. Three Everton players scored in an FA Cup semi-final in the 1990s.
    Who is the imposter here?
    A) Daniel Amokachi B) Graham Stuart C) Matt Jackson
    D) John Ebbrell

10. Which club was Howard Kendall managing when Everton asked him
    to come to Goodison Park to take over again in 1997?
    A) Sheffield United B) Real Sociedad C) Blackburn Rovers
    D) Birmingham City

QUIZ No. 72

'THE NINE' - PART 1

Everton have nine league titles to their name. They came in 1890/91, 1914/15, 1927/28, 1931/32, 1938/39, 1962/63, 1969/70, 1984/85 and 1986/87. Here are some questions about 'the nine':

1. Which three clubs have won the league more times than Everton?

2. The lowest number of defeats Everton have suffered in winning the league is five. In which of the above seasons did that occur?

3. Between the wars, from season 1919/20 to season 1938/39, Everton won three titles, which put them level with Huddersfield Town and Arsenal during this period. True or false?

4. How many times have Everton finished runners-up for the league title?

5. I think all Evertonians know who is their top league goalscorer in a league-winning season and how many goals he got, but the last win in 1986/87 took place with the lowest number of goals by their top scorer, with a total of just 14. Who scored them?

6. Although it doesn't give a true picture, because of the changes in the number of games played over time, 1931/32 witnessed the most defeats by any Everton championship-winning side in a season. How many did they lose?

7. Who is the only man to be leading scorer in more than one Everton championship-winning team?

8. In Everton's first three post-war titles, the leading goalscorer was successively a Welshman, an Englishman and a Scotsman. Who were the three players?

9. One of the top goalscorers in these championship seasons came to Everton from Notts County and another left Everton to join Notts County. Who were the two players?

10. Which two London clubs have been runners-up to Everton, the first in 1931/32 and the second in 1962/63?

QUIZ No. 73

'THE NINE' - PART 2

Here are some more questions on those nine Everton league titles.

1. Although Liverpool have won the league 19 times, Everton have held the trophy for longer. Explain?

2. Which two leading goalscorers in the title years both joined Everton from Burnley?

3. In which of the title-winning seasons did Everton get away with claiming the league despite six home defeats?

4. Who are the only Midlands club to be runners-up to Everton? It happened in 1938/39.

5. In seven of the nine league-winning seasons, Everton played 42 games, and in one of them they played 38. The first one, in 1890/91, comprised how many matches?

6. Which two Yorkshire clubs have finished runners-up to Everton, the first in 1927/28 and the second in 1969/70?

7. 1969/70 saw their highest points total with two points for a win, and 1984/85 saw their highest points total with three points for a win. What were the two points totals?

8. Who are the only club to twice be runners-up to Everton?

9. The highest number of goals Everton achieved in a title-winning season was 116. In which season did it happen?

10. In which of these nine seasons did they have the best goals-per-game ratio?

OPENING DAYS

1. Only one club has bumped into Everton 12 times on the season's opening day, that dozen being reached very recently. Who are they?
   A) Arsenal B) Chelsea C) Manchester United D) Spurs

2. Everton have started just four seasons outside the top flight and played away on the first day on three of those occasions. The only time they hosted a second-tier game on the opening day at Goodison Park was on 23 August 1952, when they lost 2-0 to which club?
   A) Blackburn Rovers B) Hull City C) Nottingham Forest
   D) Sheffield United

3. Which two clubs, one from the south of the country and one from the Midlands, are the only two that Everton have started a season against in both the top division and the one beneath it?

4. When Everton dropped out of Division One for the first time in 1929/30, they opened the next season on a ground more westerly than any they have started a season on before or since. Where did they win 3-2 on 30 August 1930?

5. In 1963, 1964 and 1965 an Everton player scored on the season's opening day, while another player carried on the sequence by doing so in 1966, 1967 and 1968. Who were the two men?

6. In 1893, 1894, 1895 and 1896 Goodison Park played host to the teams of just one city on the opening day. Which one?

7. On 2 September 1914 Joe Clennell became the first Everton player to score a hat-trick on the opening day when Everton won 3-1 in the capital. On which ground?

8. Between the end of the war and the end of the century, the depressing feeling of starting a new season at home with a 0-0 draw happened just twice at Goodison Park. The second time was a 0-0 with Aston Villa on 15 August 1998. The previous occasion was on 17 August 1974, and the team that drew with them went on to win the league despite Everton winning the return 1-0 with a Bob Latchford goal. Who were they?

9. Which Everton player scored a hat-trick in a 4-0 win at Goodison on the first day of the 1988/89 season against Newcastle United?

10. On 18 August 1956, who became the first and last team to score five times against Everton on the opening day of the season when they won 5-1 in Yorkshire?

QUIZ No. 75

POST-WAR HAT-TRICKS

1. Which southern club did Joe Royle register two hat-tricks against, the first in September 1969 and the second in November 1971, both times at Goodison Park?

2. In the three seasons Everton spent in the Second Division in the early 1950s, one player scored four hat-tricks. These came against Hull City, Oldham Athletic, Plymouth Argyle and Rotherham United. Who was he?

3. Gary Lineker managed three hat-tricks in his one season at Goodison Park in 1985/86. They came against a team from Manchester, a team from Birmingham and a team from the south coast. Can you name all three?

4. Notts County spent three years in the top flight in the early 1980s. Whose hat-trick in Everton's 4-1 win over them on 4 February 1984 helped to relegate them?

5. Bob Latchford got hat-tricks against three London clubs who have all experienced ground sharing at some point in the post-war era. Who are the three clubs?

6. Which Everton player's hat-trick contributed to a 5-1 away win in the League Cup on 7 October 1986 against Newport County?

7. Which Everton player got a hat-trick away to both Wolves and Huddersfield Town in the 1947/48 season, and followed up in September of the following season at home with another against Preston North End?

8. Apart from his many other achievements, Harry Catterick became the first Everton manager to have previously scored a hat-trick for them. It came in London in a 5-1 Everton win on 7 October 1950. Who were they playing?

9. Who scored Everton's last Premier League hat-trick of the old millennium, on 8 May 1999, in a 6-0 home win over West Ham United?

10. The same club were involved in Everton's first hat-trick of the new millennium, when the Toffees won there 4-0 on 26 February 2000. Which player scored this one?

QUIZ No. 76

POT LUCK

1. What is the link between a player who made 99 appearances for
   Everton between 1995 and 1999, arriving from Derby County
   and moving on to Blackburn Rovers, and another player who made
   19 appearances for the club between 1975 and 1980, coming from
   Wrexham and eventually rejoining them?

2. Arsenal's goalkeeper in the 1972 FA Cup final against Leeds United
   had started his career at Goodison, playing for Everton ten times, nine
   of them in the 1965/66 season. Who was he?

3. Everton have played in two League Cup finals, losing on each occasion.
   Four other clubs have played in two League Cup finals without winning
   the trophy. They are Bolton Wanderers, Southampton, Sunderland and
   West Ham United. Two of them have lost in a League Cup final to a
   team that have also beaten Everton in one. Which two?

4. Everton haven't always played in royal-blue shirts and white shorts.
   From their foundation in 1878, which two kits did they wear before the
   current one?

5. Which man who shared his first name with the title of an album by
   The Who and his surname with a post-war American President played
   73 times for Everton in the league before his transfer to Blackburn
   Rovers in 1955?

6. The 4-4 draw between Everton and Liverpool at Goodison in the
   FA Cup fifth round on 20 February 1991 is still talked about on
   Merseyside. Which two members of the Everton team that night went
   on to win the league title with other clubs?

7. Which player did Everton buy in the 1960s and sell for exactly double
   what they paid for him in the 1970s?

8. Everton's five FA Cup final wins have come against Newcastle United,
   Manchester City, Sheffield Wednesday, Watford and Manchester
   United. On two of those occasions, they were beating a team who
   hadn't previously won the cup. Which two?

9. Everton's top scorer in the 1902/03 season shares his surname with a post-war England cricket captain. What is that surname?

10. Which club have Everton lost both an FA Cup final and a League Cup final to by the same score 80 years apart?

QUIZ No. 77

SEEING RED AGAINST THE BLUES

1. Newcastle United's players seem to make a habit of getting themselves an early bath whenever they play Everton. One of them went that way when Everton won 3-0 at Goodison in 2015, another went on the same ground when the visitors lost by the same score in 2016, and in 2017 another of their players was sent off in the 94th minute when Everton won 1-0 at St. James' Park. Who were the three miscreants?

2. Which Burnley player picked up a red card when they lost 1-0 to Everton at Goodison on 18 April 2015?

3. On 18 March 2017 Hull City left Goodison beaten by 4-0. Which player left before the 90 minutes were up?

4. Which Manchester City player was sent off in their 1-1 home draw with Everton on 21 August 2017?

5. Which Brighton player saw red when his team lost 2-0 at Goodison on 10 March 2018?

6. Which cultured Stoke City midfielder demonstrated another side of his game that Gareth Bale already knew about when Everton won 2-1 away on 17 March 2018?

7. Which Southampton player was no saint when they drew 1-1 at Goodison on 5 May 2018?

8. Which Leicester City defender received his marching orders when they lost 2-1 at home to Everton on 25 August 2018?

9. Which Wolves defender didn't make it to the end of the game when Everton beat them 3-2 at Goodison on 1 September 2019?

10. When Everton drew 1-1 with Spurs at Goodison on 3 November 2019, which visiting player was sent off?

STICKY TOFFEE (SENDINGS OFF)

1. Which Everton player was sent off at Goodison when they lost 1-0 at home to Arsenal in the fourth round of the League Cup on 8 November 2006?

2. Which player left it to the very last moment of the season to be sent off when getting his marching orders in the 96th minute in a 3-1 win over Newcastle United on 13 May 2012?

3. Which Everton player was sent off when they won 2-0 against Spurs at White Hart Lane on 26 August 2005?

4. Which Everton player, against Chelsea at Goodison in the eighth minute on 12 February 2005, decided to produce a creative variation on the usual boring front-on head-butt and attempted one to the back of his opponent's head, seeking a bit of variety? All he got for his trouble was a red card.

5. As the 2010/11 season came to its close, Everton lost 1-0 at West Brom in their penultimate game, on 14 May 2011. Which player received a red card?

6. There was still time for one more that season and it came on the last day at Goodison, on 22 May 2011, when which Everton player didn't last the 90 minutes in their 1-0 win over Chelsea?

7. Which Everton player was sent off in a 2-0 win at home to Manchester City in the Premier League on 16 March 2013?

8. Which Everton forward was dismissed at Charlton Athletic on 28 December 2004, seven minutes from the end of a 2-0 defeat? Probably just getting in a little training for New Year's Eve three days later!

9. Who was sent off two minutes into added time when Everton won 2-1 at West Ham United on 22 December 2012?

10. Which Everton man was sent off in the Merseyside derby at Goodison on 1 October 2011?

QUIZ No. 79

STICKY TOFFEE (SECOND HELPING ANYONE?)

1. Who was sent off when Everton won 1-0 at Huddersfield on 29 January 2019?

2. Who scored for Everton in a 1-1 draw at Watford on 9 April 2016 but was sent off four days later in another draw, 0-0 this time, at Crystal Palace?

3. Who received a red card when Everton lost 2-1 at Turf Moor against Burnley on 3 March 2018?

4. Everton usually find Arsenal a difficult proposition. Who didn't help things by getting sent off when they lost 5-2 at home to the Londoners on 22 October 2017?

5. Which Everton player was given his marching orders in the 2-2 draw at Bournemouth on 25 August 2018?

6. Who was sent off two minutes from the end of Everton's 1-1 draw at Manchester City on 21 August 2017?

7. Which Everton player saw red twice, firstly in a 0-0 draw at Swansea in 2015, and secondly in a 3-2 home defeat by West Ham United in 2016?

8. The same thing happened to another Everton player, but this time both offences occurred in 2015, both near the end of games at Chelsea and Arsenal. Who was the culprit?

9. Who received a very late red card in the 95th minute in a 1-0 defeat at Watford on 9 February 2019?

10. Who scored Everton's goal in a 1-1 home draw with Southampton on 16 April 2016, but was sent off four days later against Liverpool?

QUIZ No. 80

TOP TOFFEES - No. 1 - ALAN BALL

1. This small package of class and energy was one third of Everton's finest midfield in the second half of the 1960s and all too little of the 1970s. He played for four other league clubs. Most people remember three of them. Can you name all four?

2. Despite being more a provider of chances for others, he topped Everton's goalscoring charts in his first two seasons at the club and scored on the opening day in his first match for the club on 20 August 1966 in a 1-0 win in London. Who did Everton play that day?

3. He scored 78 goals for Everton in all competitions and his total number of games for the club had a nice look to it. What was that number?

4. He endeared himself to the Goodison faithful by scoring twice in a 3-1 league win over Liverpool and then grabbing the winner in a fifth-round FA Cup tie between the clubs. Before that FA Cup goal, he had scored his first one for Everton in a 1-1 away draw in the Midlands in the fourth round. On which ground?

5. In 1968 one club took a right hammering from Alan Ball. Away from home on 16 March 1968, he hit four in Everton's 6-2 win, and then in the next season on 28 September his hat-trick formed the largest part of their 4-0 home win against the same club. Who were Everton's unfortunate Midlands opponents?

6. In 1969/70 he was the only Everton player to score in the first game of both domestic cup competitions. In the League Cup Everton won 1-0 away to a team from the North East who had to apply for re-election at the end of that season, while in the FA Cup he got Everton's goal in a 2-1 defeat in the third round in Yorkshire. Which two teams did he score against?

7. In his English career, Alan Ball played in 743 league games and started in all of them, never coming on as a substitute. True or false?

8. Winning the league with Everton must have been his biggest moment in league football, but there was probably nothing to top winning the World Cup in 1966 with England. It was achieved on his 14th cap. Who were the only two members of that famous side with fewer caps to their name on the day?

9. He won 72 England caps and scored eight goals for his country. Strangely, seven of them were away, with the other coming at Wembley. He scored in Sweden, Austria, Wales, Belgium, Columbia and Scotland. Which of those constituted the only occasion on which he scored twice in a game for England?

10. As a manager, which club did Alan Ball get promoted to the top flight in 1986/87, a club that had last played at that level in the late 1950s?

QUIZ No. 81

TOP TOFFEES - No. 2 - DIXIE DEAN

1. They don't come any bigger in Everton folklore than this man, and his 349 goals for the club from 399 league games will almost certainly stand for ever. Which two other league clubs did he play for?

2. On which now-defunct London ground did he make his Everton debut on 21 March 1925?

3. Dean's 60 league goals in the 1927/28 season has stood as a record for nearly a century now and is unlikely ever to be beaten, but that's what they said about the 59 goals that a certain Middlesbrough forward scored the season before Dixie's record haul. Which player must have been amazed and depressed that his record stood for just one year?

4. Opposition from one city provided Dean with his first Everton goal on 28 March 1925 at Goodison Park and his last Everton appearance at the same place on 11 December 1937. Which two clubs were involved?

5. Another city's two teams were slaughtered in consecutive weeks by Dean's goalscoring exploits. On 10 October 1931 Everton won 5-1 away with a Dean hat-trick, and then on the 17th they beat another of the city's clubs 9-3 at Goodison when his contribution was five. Which city's two clubs were beaten?

6. Bill Dean had a great record against this particular club. In his first Everton season of 1925/26, they were the only club he scored a hat-trick against both home and away, and he got another against them in a 5-2 Goodison win in December 1928. Then in the Charity Shield on 12 October 1932 on their own ground he subjected them to a four-timer in Everton's 5-3 win. Not a lot of charity on show there! Who were this northern club?

7. On 7 February 1931 Everton won 7-0 in the capital. It was the only time Dixie Dean scored three times in the season they won the Second Division title. Who did they beat?
A) Charlton Athletic B) Millwall C) QPR D) Spurs

8. Which Midlands club are the only team that Dean scored a hat-trick against three times at Goodison Park, the first coming in a 7-1 win in 1927, the second in a 9-2 win in which he got four in 1931, and the last in a 6-3 win in 1933?

9. Anfield, Turf Moor and Fratton Park are three grounds that are thankfully still going strong today. What did Dixie Dean do on those grounds in the league that he failed to do on any other away grounds?

10. The same club provided the opposition at Goodison Park when Bill Dean broke the scoring record on the last day of the 1927/28 season, and when he scored what would turn out to be his last Everton goal on the opening day of the 1937/38 season. Who were they?

QUIZ No. 82

TOP TOFFEES - No. 3 - PETER FARRELL

1. A powerhouse of a wing-half and a great captain of an often poor side, Peter Farrell was an inspiration from the moment he arrived from Shamrock Rovers in 1946, playing 453 games in all competitions for the club. It is very rare for a player to be capped by Northern Ireland and the Republic, but Peter played seven times for the former and 28 for the latter. Which Everton manager also played for both?

2. Peter Farrell made his debut in a 2-1 defeat on 23 November 1946 at a now-defunct Midlands ground named after a monarch. Which one?

3. His first goal for Everton came at Goodison Park in a 4-1 win on 20 December 1947 against which Lancashire club?

4. He scored 17 goals in total for Everton but failed to score against Liverpool. True or false?

5. He scored four FA Cup goals for the Blues, the first of them coming against Grimsby Town in a 4-1 away win in 1948, but which two London clubs exited from the competition at Goodison in the successive years of 1956 and 1957 after he had scored against them?

6. His only other FA Cup goal was in the great second-half fightback in the 1952/53 semi-final when Everton came from 0-4 to 3-4 against which club?

7. On 21 September 1949 he was part of the Republic of Ireland side that beat England 2-0, scoring one of the goals. Where was the match played and what was significant about it?

8. Peter Farrell never missed a league game in 1950/51 and 1955/56, and over the ten-year period of 1947/48 to 1956/57, he played in all but 25 of the club's 420 league games. True or false?

9. He must have been exhausted by the time he left Goodison as a 35-year-old, but he still managed to play another 114 times for which club?

10. Which other Everton player joined the club from Shamrock Rovers, also played over 400 times for Everton and left to join the same club as Peter Farrell in 1957?

QUIZ No. 83

TOP TOFFEES - No. 4 - COLIN HARVEY

1. Colin Harvey was a superb midfielder in a superb midfield whose brilliance culminated in the league title in 1970. His Everton debut must have been an awesome and rather terrifying experience for an 18-year-old on that September night in 1963. Where did it take place and who were Everton playing?

2. That night ended in defeat, but that was far from the case when he scored his first goal for Everton in a 4-0 away win on which ground?

3. His first FA Cup goal for Everton came on 13 January 1965 in a third-round replay that Everton won 3-0 away from home against the club that Colin eventually joined in 1974. Who were they?

4. Although he probably should have won a lot more, he received his only England cap in a 1-0 away win against Malta on 3 February 1971. Which other Everton player made his international debut in that game?

5. The only criticism you could offer concerning Colin Harvey was that he might have scored more goals, given his qualities. The most vital one he got came against which club in the FA Cup semi-final of 1966, giving Everton their passport to Wembley?

6. He scored a great goal against this club in the title-clinching game in 1970, and they were also the only side he scored against in three Everton home games. Who were they?

7. Colin Harvey played in both of Everton's 1960s FA Cup finals, but with a different number on his back each time. What were those two numbers, one in 1966 and the other in 1968?

8. On 24 August 1971, for the only time in his career, Colin Harvey got two goals in a game. They were the two that beat which London club 2-0 at Goodison that day?

9. One London ground was the only one on which he scored away for Everton on three separate occasions, and another was the last ground he scored on for Everton in the FA Cup, it coming in a 2-2 draw in the third round of the 1971/72 season. What are the two grounds?

10. His managerial career was far less successful than his playing one and suffered from too many draws. In fact, concerning the three main domestic competitions, Everton drew more games than they won under his tenure. He got the sack in November 1990, when Howard Kendall took over again. What happened six days later that told everyone, in case they didn't already know, that this man was a Blue to his roots?

QUIZ No. 84

TOP TOFFEES - No. 5 - HOWARD KENDALL

1. Much loved in the blue half of the city, Howard Kendall was successful at Everton in two capacities, those of player and manager. He played for four other league clubs besides Everton. Who were they?

2. His first Everton goal came on 5 September 1967 in a 2-0 win against a London club at Goodison. He also scored on their ground in the same season, one of only two times he scored home and away against a club, the other being Sunderland. Who were this London club?

3. His first FA Cup goal for the Toffees was on their run to the final in 1968 when they won 3-1 away in the sixth round against which Midlands club?

4. In his first full season he scored the only goal of the game in two league games at Goodison, one in February 1968 and the other the following month. Who were the two beaten clubs?

5. Howard Kendall scored two goals in a game just twice in his career. The first came in a 5-0 win at Goodison in the FA Cup sixth round on 6 March 1971 against a southern club from the fourth tier of English football who were having the greatest cup run in their history until that point. The second was in a 3-1 league win at Goodison Park on 16 December 1972 against a London club. Who were the two defeated sides?

6. Kendall scored at home on more than one occasion against three clubs during his time at Everton. He did so against Newcastle United, Ipswich Town and a London club. Which one?
A) Arsenal B) Chelsea C) Spurs D) West Ham United

7. Howard Kendall had an unprecedented three spells as Everton's manager. The first spell, in the 1980s, was about as good as it gets. The other two, in the 1990s, were underwhelming. His first game in charge, on 29 August 1982, and his very last game in charge, on 10 May 1998, were both against clubs from the Midlands. Which two?

8. Which three managers did he replace, firstly in 1981, then in 1990, and finally in 1997?

9. Which three English clubs besides Everton did he manage?

10. Still the last Englishman to manage an English club to European silverware, besides England, in which other country has he managed more than one club?

QUIZ No. 85

TOP TOFFEES - No. 6 - BRIAN LABONE

1. The rock at the heart of Everton's defence for well over 500 matches, this model professional was utterly reliable and his career stretched over three decades between 1957 and 1971. Why, in 1967, did it look for a while that it might not reach that third decade?

2. Which Midlands club did he make his debut against in a 2-1 defeat away from home on 29 March 1958?

3. It seems that he wasn't waved forward at corners overmuch because he scored just twice in the league for Everton and both of them came against Lancastrian opposition whose names begin with the same letter. They both came in the 1965/66 season, one in a 2-2 home draw and the other in a 1-1 away draw. Who were the two opponents?

4. Brian Labone was the first Everton player to reach 450 league appearances for the club. True or false?

5. As captain of the team closing in on the league title in 1970, he would have been gutted to pick up an injury with just eight games to go. Who took over the centre-half role for those eight vital remaining games?

6. Why could you say that Brian Labone was sandwiched between Ron Yeats and Dave Mackay?

7. Seasons 1960/61, 1961/62, 1962/63, 1964/65, 1966/67 and 1968/69 comprised 252 league matches. How many did he miss in those six seasons?

8. He was capped 26 times for his country, and but for Jack Charlton's consistency it would have been quite a few more. His first cap came away to Northern Ireland in a 3-1 win on 20 October 1962. Which future Everton team-mate was also playing for England that day?

9. His last cap was a very unhappy moment for English football, when England lost a World Cup quarter-final 3-2 to West Germany after holding a 2-0 lead. An Everton regular from the current century has a first name that was the venue for England's game that day. What was it?

10. Which former Evertonian said after Brian's death, 'Brian was Everton. If you could put together a team of every player that has ever captained Everton, every one of us would turn to Brian to lead us out. He will always be known as the captain of Everton'?

QUIZ No. 86

TOP TOFFEES – No. 7 – KEVIN RATCLIFFE

1. Very quick and tough, with a sharp defensive mindset, Kevin Ratcliffe led Everton to more success than any other club captain in the 1980s. His debut came in a 0-0 away draw on 12 March 1980 at a sizeable stadium. Where?

2. He won 59 Welsh caps and led them as well. His first cap, on 19 November 1980, came in a 1-0 win over Czechoslovakia, while his last appearance for his country came after he had left Goodison, on 31 March 1993 against Belgium in a 2-0 home win. Both his first and last matches for Wales were in the same city but on different grounds. Which two grounds were involved?

3. Like his great predecessor, Brian Labone, goals were thin on the ground and he actually never felt the joy of scoring at Goodison Park. True or false?

4. Some joy was to be had on two away grounds, the first in January of 1983 when he got the only goal of the game, and the second in February of 1986 when he got a superb goal in a 2-0 away win that would have pleased him no end! What were the two grounds he scored on?

5. A tougher question. What links those two goals, apart from the fact that they were the only two away goals of his career with Everton?

6. Although he came close, Kevin Ratcliffe never managed to play every league game of a season for Everton. True or false?

7. The club he left Everton for in 1992 were also the only team he scored for besides Everton. Who were they?

8. Which two clubs beginning with a 'D' did he turn out for a handful of times in the early to mid-90s?

9. Which club were the only one that he both played for and managed?

10. On 5 January 2003 Kevin Ratcliffe did what every former player who becomes a manager with another club loves to do, and that is to knock his old club out of the FA Cup. Which club that he was managing beat Everton 2-1 on that day and why did it have added significance for the beaten Everton manager David Moyes?

QUIZ No. 87

TOP TOFFEES - No. 8 - PETER REID

1. Peter Reid was the bundle of energy that was the crucial link between attack and defence in that 1980s Everton side. Hard as nails, he nevertheless played the game in a great spirit; his battles with Steve McMahon spring to mind. From which club did Everton buy him in 1982 and which club did he move to in 1989?

2. He played the same number of times for England as the total number of goals he scored for Everton. What was that number?
   A) 10 B) 11 C) 12 D) 13

3. Which London club was the only one he scored against in more than one game at Goodison and also the only club he scored against in the League Cup?

4. Discounting London, which city was the only one where he scored against both their clubs? His goals came in a 1-0 away win in 1983 and a 5-0 home win in 1984?

5. He was inspirational in the run to the title and the European Cup Winners' Cup in 1985. What proved to be his solitary goal in Europe for Everton came on 20 March 1985 in the away leg against which club who were beaten 2-0 on the night in that quarter-final?

6. His first England cap came as a substitute for a Manchester United midfielder against Mexico in 1985 and his last cap in 1988 was as a substitute for another Manchester United midfielder. Who were the two players?

7. Which London club were the only team he scored against at home and away in league football for Everton?
   A) Arsenal B) Chelsea C) Spurs D) West Ham United

8. Peter Reid scored three FA Cup goals for Everton. The last of them was against Sheffield Wednesday in the first meeting of their 1988 marathon, but earlier he had twice contributed to 3-0 Goodison Park fifth-round wins over two teams who are a stone's throw from each other. The first of them were playing in the second flight at the time, although they were usually in the third, while the other were a non-league club. Who were the two teams?

9. Peter's last Everton goal came in a 2-1 away win against Charlton Athletic on 12 November 1988, when Graeme Sharp scored their other goal. On which ground was the match played?

10. Who were the only club Peter Reid played for and managed?

QUIZ No. 88

TOP TOFFEES - No. 9 - NEVILLE SOUTHALL

1. Goalkeeping longevity has been the key at Everton and between them Ted Sagar, Jimmy O'Neill, Albert Dunlop, Gordon West and Neville Southall have made well over 2,000 appearances for the Toffees. Neville was signed by Howard Kendall for £150,000 from Bury in 1981 and in 1985 became the first Evertonian to win the Football Writers' Association Player of the Year award and the fourth – and so far last – goalkeeper to win it. The other three won it with Manchester City, Stoke City and Spurs. Who were they?

2. Neville Southall holds the Everton appearances record for the most league games, the most FA Cup ties and the most League Cup ties. His overall score in all competitions puts you in mind of an aeroplane. Why?

3. He was capped 92 times by Wales and held the record for some years before which player went past him in 2018?

4. Although his clubs run into double figures, he has played over 50 times for just one other club, where he also won their Player of the Year award in 1998/99. Which club was it?

5. Having become a goalkeeping coach in the Premier League, an injury crisis meant that he had to play himself on 12 March 2000 at the age of 41 years and 178 days. Who did he play for and which club from the same county beat them 2-1 on the day?

6. Which club did Everton beat 2-1 at Goodison Park on the occasion of Neville Southall's debut for the club on 17 October 1981?

7. In how many seasons during his Everton career did Southall play every league game?

8. How many FA Cup finals did Southall play in goal for Everton in, and how many goals did he concede in those games?

9. Neville Southall took charge of one international for Wales, when they lost 2-0 to Denmark at Anfield on 9 June 1999. Which manager did he take over from and who did he hand the job on to?

10. Which three unlikely non-league clubs on the south coast has he managed for short periods?

QUIZ No. 89

TOP TOFFEES - No. 10 - ROY VERNON

1. A bargain buy at £27,000, Roy Vernon was the captain of the first Everton side post-war to win the league title. A class act with a powerful shot, he scored in a 3-1 win back at the home of his former club in March 1961 and then scored the winner against them in the following season at Goodison. Who did they sign him from?

2. He played four full seasons at Everton and was the club's leading league goalscorer in all of them. True or false?

3. After over 200 appearances and over 100 goals in all competitions for Everton, he played 87 league games for another club from 1965 onwards before finishing with just four games for a Yorkshire club who are no longer in the league. Which two clubs are they?

4. He played 32 times for Wales, 13 of them while with the Toffees, making his debut in 1957 against Northern Ireland and scoring his first goal for his country in his second game, the winner against Czechoslovakia in Cardiff. His first international goal as an Everton player came at the same venue on 22 October 1960 in a 2-0 win over which nation?

5. He lit up Goodison Park with nine goals in his first 12 games and scored in the legendary first meeting between the two Merseyside clubs in eight years, which took place in September 1962 at Goodison. The next season saw him score home and away to Liverpool, which does help to get the fans on your side. The last time an Everton player had performed that feat was before the war, in the 1938/39 title-winning season. Which player did it that year, when Everton won 2-1 at home and 3-0 away?
    A) Stan Bentham B) Wally Boyes C) Tommy Lawton
    D) Alex Stevenson

6. Who did Roy Vernon take over the captaincy from and which player in turn did he hand it over to briefly before Brian Labone later made it his?

7. Roy's first domestic cup goal for Everton came on 31 October 1960 in the new competition known as the League Cup. His goal formed part of their 3-1 home win over which Midlands club from two divisions below them who were promoted that season?
    A) Coventry City B) Mansfield Town C) Notts County
    D) Walsall

8. On which now-defunct London ground did Roy Vernon score his first Everton goal when they lost 2-1 on 20 February 1960?

9. In the FA Cup of 1963/64, in the fourth round, he scored home and away against the same club in the competition. Everton had drawn 1-1 in Yorkshire and won the replay 2-0. Who were their opponents?

10. The last question concerns three Roy Vernon hat-tricks that came in 1961 in a 4-1 win over Arsenal, in 1962 in an 8-3 win over Cardiff City, and in 1963 in a 4-1 win over Fulham, all three coming at Goodison Park. What else links them together?

QUIZ No. 90

TOP TOFFEES - No. 11 - DAVE WATSON

1. Dave Watson was a massive presence at the heart of the Everton defence for the best part of 15 years. For which club had he already played over 200 league games when he came to Goodison in 1986, and to which club did he go as manager when his playing career ended in 2001?

2. On 22 August 1986, did Everton pay more or less than one million pounds for his signature?

3. His first Everton game was on 23 August 1986 at Goodison Park and he started with a 2-0 win. His last Everton game was also at Goodison Park on 15 January 2000 and finished 2-2. The two teams they played on these occasions met in the 1991 FA Cup final. Who were they?

4. He was Everton's captain when they won the FA Cup against Manchester United in 1995. Which other trophy did he captain a side to win in his career?

5. He received 12 England caps and his debut coincided with arguably the finest moment in the career of John Barnes. Who did England beat on his debut?

6. Against which Yorkshire club did he score his first Everton goal in a 2-0 win at Goodison on 17 January 1987?

7. In the third round of the League Cup in 1993/94, he scored in a 2-2 draw with a London club at Goodison. In the replay he scored twice as Everton won 4-1. Who did they beat?

8. Which two clubs has he got the winner against at Goodison in the FA Cup, the first time in a fifth-round second replay in 1991, and the second time in the sixth round on the way to winning it in 1995?

9. Which London club has he scored against in four league matches at Goodison?

10. In league football, he has scored home and away against four clubs. They are Sheffield Wednesday, Southampton, Arsenal and one other. Who are missing?

QUIZ No. 91

TOP TOFFEES - No. 12 - ALEX YOUNG

1. This elegant centre-forward brought a different dimension to that role and his time on the ball and positional sense made him such a favourite with the fans that they invented a phrase to describe him. What was it?

2. He was plagued with blisters on his feet throughout his career but played through the pain. He scored 77 times in his 228 league games for the club, but played in all 42 matches in just one season. Which one?

3. Everton swooped to purchase his signature in November 1960 after his headline-attracting performances in Scotland. Which club sold him to Everton and who else did they buy at the same time from the same club, who played 73 games for Everton before leaving for Brentford?

4. His first Scottish cap came while he was still playing in that country. The venue was Hampden Park and the game with England ended 1-1. On the England team that day was someone who would later be a Goodison team-mate but was still at that time with another club and was, like Young, making his international debut. Who was he?

5. He scored five goals for his country in eight games, an insultingly low number of appearances. The Scottish selectors didn't like players who'd moved to England and froze Young out. In his first game for Scotland after his move to Everton, he scored twice in a 3-0 away win on 7 May 1961 and was then given just one more cap an astonishing five years later! Who did he grab the two goals against?

6. Two Lancastrian clubs whose names start with the same letter figure in this question. Which one did he score his first Everton goals against, when he scored twice in a 3-1 away win on 31 March 1961, and which one did he score against at Goodison three seasons running, starting with 1961/62, totalling five goals in the three games?

7. Because Everton tried the new League Cup out in Young's first season and then didn't enter it again until his last season, he bookended his time at Goodison with his only goals in the competition, coming against two clubs beginning with 'S'. The first was in an embarrassing 2-1 defeat in the fifth round on 15 February 1961, and the second was when he scored twice in a 3-2 home defeat on 11 October 1967. Which two clubs did they play?

8. Alex Young's only Everton hat-trick came at Goodison Park on 31 August 1965 in a 5-1 win over which Yorkshire club?

9. He scored twice in an FA Cup tie just once. It came against a Lancastrian club in a third-round replay at Goodison on 31 January 1967, when his brace won the game 2-1. Who did they beat?

10. The last goal Alex scored for Everton came in a 3-1 away defeat on 16 December 1967 on a famous ground. Not far from that ground, Young played 23 games for a club in the third flight of English football the following season. What was the ground and who were the club he played for?

QUIZ No. 92

TRANSFERS - 1888-1950

As there are very few people around now who would have seen any of these players, I've been very liberal with my clues to the players' identities.

1. Walter Balmer made 293 league appearances for Everton between 1897 and 1907 and was a member of the FA Cup-winning side of 1906. He came to Everton from South Shore. Who did they eventually become?

2. He came from Blackburn Rovers in 1900 and left for Preston North End in 1907 after playing in 175 league games for the Blues. His full name is the same as that of Manchester City's centre-half in the 1969 FA Cup final. Who was he?

3. Bert Freeman knew where the net was. After coming to Merseyside from Arsenal in 1907 he scored 63 goals in 86 games for Everton before moving to Burnley in 1911. What did he do while at Turf Moor that Evertonians would have been delighted by?

4. This man played exactly 50 league games for Everton and scored 18 goals between 1920 and 1922, arriving from Sunderland and departing for West Ham United. He shared his first name with the most famous comedian of the era and his surname with the only goalkeeper to stop a Matt Le Tissier penalty. Have you got it now?

5. Neil McBain came from Manchester United in 1923 and played 97 league games for Everton before going back to his native Scotland with St Johnstone in 1925. When he was 51 and long retired in 1947 he entered the record books. Why?

6. Which member of Everton's FA Cup-winning side of 1933 came to the club from Hibernian in 1928 and left for Exeter City in 1935, 140 games and 42 goals later?

7. Edgar Chadwick was a consistent goalscorer for Everton between 1888 and 1899, running up a total of 97 goals in 270 games. The Lancashire club he came from and the club from the same county he went to after his Everton years don't really like each other much. Who are they?

8. A player by the name of Gillick came from Rangers in 1935 and went back there in 1945, scoring 40 goals in 121 games for Everton between those dates. He has the very rare distinction of having a political party for a first name. Is it Labour, Tory, Liberal or Green?

9. This man came from Newcastle United in 1888 and left for Preston North End without troubling the statisticians. In 1891 he was back again and this time made 89 appearances for Everton before returning to his Scottish roots with Dundee. His first name is a three-letter palindrome and his surname is a northern jumps track. What was his name?

10. This player was a key man in the 1927/28 title-winning Everton team and never missed a single league game that season. He came from Dundee in 1923 and went back to the same club 249 Everton games later. Who was he?

QUIZ No. 93

TRANSFERS - 1951-89

1. Which left-sided defender came from Sheffield Wednesday in 1973 and played in 83 league games for the Toffees?

2. From his initials it sounds like he might be useful if your car broke down! He made just 12 appearances for Everton between 1957 and 1960 before joining Luton Town. Later in his career this inside-forward was a member of the Preston North End side beaten by West Ham United in the 1964 FA Cup final. Who was he?

3. Luton Town appear again in this question because they signed an Irishman that had been at Goodison between 1950 and 1953. He had played for Everton 29 times in all competitions but got more opportunities at Luton, appearing in their losing FA Cup final side in 1959. Who was he?

4. Which left-back joined Everton from Scunthorpe United in 1985 and after 101 league games for the Merseysiders left for Manchester City in 1990?

5. Bruce Rioch came from this club in 1976, played 30 times for the blues and then in the following season rejoined the club he had left. Who were they?

6. Which tricky winger came from QPR in 1977 and made 71 appearances for Everton before a move to Wolves in 1979?

7. After being a key figure in the push for the title in 1970 Alan Whittle went south to the capital in 1972 after 74 league outings. Who did he join?

8. Everton broke their transfer record and paid their first half a million for this midfielder from Nottingham Forest in 1979. He moved on to Manchester City in 1981 after 81 league games. Who was he, and for a bonus point which other club in Lancashire did he also play exactly 81 league games for?

9. A familiar figure at Goodison during the 1980s, he joined the club from the other side of Stanley Park in 1983 and left for Sheffield Wednesday in 1988, but not before playing for Everton in 177 league games. Who was he?

10. This is a difficult one because this guy played just once for Everton. What do you mean you weren't at the game! A Welsh international, he left for Scunthorpe United in 1960, but in 1971 he captained Aston Villa in the League Cup final against Spurs at Wembley. Have you got it now?

QUIZ No. 94

TRANSFERS - 1990-2005

1. Which Everton striker returned to his old club in 1994 after frustratingly scoring 99 times for the Toffees in all competitions? In his new role with Sky Sports he has also often found that elusive goal difficult to come by!

2. Which player moved on to Sheffield Wednesday in 1998 after over 200 appearances for the Blues in all competitions since signing from Manchester City at the start of the decade?

3. Which midfielder left Everton for Birmingham City in 1996 after playing over 150 times in all competitions for Everton since arriving from Southampton in 1992?

4. Who came to Goodison from Grimsby Town in 1997 and departed for Sunderland in 1999 after making exactly 50 appearances for the club in all competitions?

5. He wasn't a centre-forward and he wasn't a centre-half but he was one of the finest headers of a ball I've ever seen. He played 65 times for Everton after joining the club from Leeds United in 1996 and moved on to Newcastle United in 1998. Who was he?

6. Which Everton player, who made 64 appearances for the club in all competitions after coming from Monaco to Merseyside in 1998, moved on to Fulham in 2000?

7. Which Everton player, who scored 15 goals in 68 league games for the club, left for Blackburn Rovers in 1991, two years after arriving from Leicester City?

8. Who came to Goodison Park via Aston Villa in 2000 and, after making 126 Premier League appearances for the Blues, joined West Brom in 2005?

9. Who played 139 times for Everton after signing from Motherwell in 2003, before a move to Birmingham City four years later?

10. Who joined Everton from Sunderland in 2003, making over 120 appearances for the Toffees in all competitions before moving on to Wigan Athletic?

TRANSFERS - 2006-20

1. Between 2013 and 2015 Everton bought two players from Barnsley. Both subsequently moved on, one to Manchester City and the other to West Brom. Who were the two players?

2. Who came from Wolves in 2006 and left for Manchester City in 2009 after 113 games for Everton in the Premier League?

3. Whose time at Everton took in 40 games in all competitions in 2010 and 2011 and was sandwiched between spells at Leeds United and Leicester City?

4. During this period one much-loved Evertonian returned to Sheffield United and another player made it big at Everton after arriving from that club. Who are the two men?

5. Which Everton defender made 60 Premier League appearances for the club after his move from Swansea City in 2016 before trying his luck at Stoke City on a loan deal?

6. Everton paid a record fee for this Middlesbrough front man in 2007, and after scoring 25 times in 82 league games for the club he moved to Blackburn Rovers in 2011 after a loan spell at Leicester City. Who was he?

7. Another striker's Everton career from 2006 to 2008 was in the middle of two spells with London clubs, namely Crystal Palace and Fulham. He scored 17 goals in 61 league outings for Everton. Who was he?

8. Two players left Arsenal for Everton in 2018 and 2019. One was an England international who has been dealt with elsewhere. Who was the other one?

9. Ademola Lookman eventually left Everton for Leicester City after a loan spell at Fulham. Between 2017 and 2019 he made 36 Premier League appearances for Everton, who had bought him from which club?

10. Which central defender joined Everton from Portsmouth in 2009 and left for another south-coast club in Bournemouth in 2015, between those dates making 174 Premier League appearances for Everton?

QUIZ No. 96

TRUE OR FALSE

1. In their first season of league football in 1888/89, Everton's Edgar Chadwick became their first player to appear in every league game in a season? True or false?

2. Thomas Myhre was the last player in the 20th century to play in every league game for Everton when he turned out in all 38 of their matches in 1998/99. True or false?

3. None of the following six Evertonians reached 200 league games for the club – Alan Ball, Martin Dobson, Jimmy Harris, Andy King, Alex Parker and Jimmy Stein. True or false?

4. Everton have on two occasions taken the title away from Liverpool when they held it. It has not happened twice with any other club. True or false?

5. Centre-half Glenn Keeley in the early 1980s played just one league game for Everton and managed to get sent off in the Merseyside derby. True or false?
    P.S. He did go on to have an excellent career at Blackburn Rovers.

6. Everton's biggest league defeat is 7-0. It has happened twice, firstly against Southampton in 1949 in the old First Division, and more recently against Arsenal in the Premier League in 2005. True or false?

7. The highest league position Everton have attained in the Premier League era is third. True or false?

8. When Danny Cadamarteri went out on loan to Fulham and Bradford City, he scored on his debut for both clubs. True or false?

9. Bobby Parker became Everton's top league goalscorer in a season between 1888 and World War One when he scored 36 goals for the club when they were champions in 1914/15. True or false?

10. In top-flight football, Everton have finished second in the league the same number of times they have finished third, and that number is seven. True or false?

QUIZ No. 97

VENUES

1. On which ground did Everton play in successive FA Cup finals in 1905/06 and 1906/07?

2. Besides London, in which city have Everton played an FA Cup semi-final or final on three of its grounds?

3. On which ground have Everton played the most FA Cup semi-finals?

4. On which ground more famous for cricket did Everton play FA Cup semi-final replays in 1893 and 1905?

5. In 1984 Everton made their only FA Cup semi-final appearance on a London club ground when they beat Southampton at which venue?

6. On which ground have Everton played in four FA Cup semi-finals or replays without winning?

7. Old Trafford has not been a great semi-final venue for Everton in the FA Cup. Of four matches played there they have lost three. Their only win came in the 1968 semi-final. Who did they beat 1-0?

8. On which now-defunct Lancastrian ground have Everton got a 100 per cent FA Cup semi-final record by winning there on their only two visits, in 1907 and 1966?

9. On which Yorkshire ground have Everton won, drawn and lost in three FA Cup semi-final visits there in 1910, 1980 and 1995?

10. In 1893, when Everton played in an FA Cup semi-final for the first time, the first two attempts to settle the issue ended in draws, one in Yorkshire and the other in Lancashire. Both venues were club grounds that are still going strong today. Which grounds were involved?

QUIZ No. 98

WHERE DID YOU COME FROM?

1. From which Spanish club did Everton sign Mikel Arteta?

2. Steven Pienaar and Thomas Gravesen both joined Everton from German clubs. Which two clubs were involved?

3. Which Turkish club did Kevin Campbell leave to come to Goodison?

4. As of 2020 Everton currently have three players who came to the club from Barcelona. Who are they?

5. Richard Gough and Joe-Max Moore both came to Everton via clubs from the USA. Which two?

6. From which club did Everton buy Johnny Heitinga and Joel Robles?

7. Two Russian clubs provided Everton with Aiden McGeady and Oumar Niasse. Which two?

8. Duncan McKenzie and Daniel Amokachi came to Merseyside from two Belgian clubs. Which two?

9. From which Dutch club did Abel Xavier sign for Everton?

10. From which club did Marouane Fellaini come to Goodison?

QUIZ No. 99

WILD CARD - PART 1

1. On 3 November 2001 Paul Gascoigne scored his only goal for Everton in a 2-2 away draw in the Premier League. Who were their Lancastrian opponents?

2. Four Evertonians were on the pitch at some stage of England's opening game against Romania in the 1970 World Cup in Mexico. Who were they?

3. Rotterdam has a special place in the hearts of Everton fans as the venue for their only European trophy win, which came in the Cup Winners' Cup of 1985. Which two other British clubs have also won that trophy in that city?

4. Terry Phelan came to Goodison from one London club at the end of one millennium, moved on to another London club at the start of the next one, and had already won the FA Cup with a third London club. Who are the three London clubs?

5. Which former PFA Footballer of the Year played seven times in all competitions for Everton in 2002?

6. Two players with the same surname were both transferred to Midlands clubs in 1979, one to Coventry City and the other to Birmingham City. Both were born in Liverpool and there were only four league appearances between them when they went, one making 86 and the other 82. What was that surname?

7. Who is the only Everton manager to also take control of a national team in four different decades?

8. In the second replay of the League Cup final of 1977 between Everton and Aston Villa it was noticed that in the first half two Everton players were wearing a number-two shirt. Who changed his to a three at half-time?

9. In this century which two players who have scored in Europe for Everton have also scored in a Champions League final?

THE ULTIMATE EVERTON QUIZ BOOK

10. Gareth Barry is a player I like a lot. He played 131 league games for Everton, and, counting all his clubs in all competitions and his England caps, his career encompassed 885 games. Why was it a shame he didn't end up with another 181 appearances?

QUIZ No. 100

WILD CARD - PART 2

1. In which competition have Everton beaten Arsenal and Blackburn Rovers in the final and lost to Chelsea, Crystal Palace, Norwich City and Aston Villa?

2. The first time Everton were allowed to have a substitute on the bench in an FA Cup final came in 1968 against West Bromwich Albion. Who remained on that bench through 120 minutes of football?

3. When Everton emerged from the Wembley tunnel for that 1968 final they were missing one scouser from the side that won the cup there in 1966, but had gained two more. Who were the three players involved?

4. Which now-defunct competition have Everton been twice runners-up in at Wembley, firstly in 1988/89 against Nottingham Forest and then again the following year against Crystal Palace?

5. Where did Everton train between 1946 and 2007, and where do they train now?

6. Who was the first man to score 100 league goals for Everton?

7. Where is Everton's proposed new ground situated and in what season is it expected to open?

8. What will be its capacity?
   A) 50,888 B) 51,888 C) 52,888 D) 53,888

9. Everton's record number of league wins in a season was set in 1969/70. How many of their 42 games did they win?

10. Who is the only Everton player to score from the penalty spot for them in an FA Cup semi-final?

ANSWERS

QUIZ No.1 ANYTHING GOES - PART 1

1. Mike Pejic
2. Gordon Lee
3. Brian Kidd
4. Ray Wilson
5. Alan Ball
6. Jeff Astle and Frank Lampard
7. Bernard
8. Joe Royle
9. Harry Grundy
10. David Ford of Sheffield Wednesday

QUIZ No.2 ANYTHING GOES - PART 2

1. Dixie Dean
2. George Harrison
3. Paul McCartney
4. China
5. St. Domingos and St. Lukes
6. He was a violinist in the Halle orchestra
7. Colin Todd
8. Ron Saunders
9. Harry Potts
10. Jock Dodds and John Willie Parker

QUIZ No.3 ASSORTED OPPONENTS

1. Stephen Ireland
2. Christian Benitez
3. Frederic Piquionne
4. Charles N'Zogbia
5. Wes Brown
6. Stewart Downing
7. Graziano Pelle
8. Victor Moses
9. Hal Robson-Kanu
10. Ricky Van Wolfswinkel

QUIZ No.4 ASSORTED TOFFEES

1. Liverpool
2. T. E. Jones and T. G. Jones
3. Tommy Lawton
4. Tommy and Billy Wright
5. Kevin Ratcliffe, Trevor Steven and Graeme Sharp
6. Old Trafford
7. Joe Royle
8. John Ebbrell
9. Duncan Ferguson
10. Dave Hickson

QUIZ No.5 AWAY FROM GOODISON (AFTER)

1. Harry Leyland and Matt Woods
2. Gerard Deulofeu
3. Pat Van den Hauwe and Gary Lineker
4. Bobby Collins
5. Paul Bracewell
6. Joe Mercer
7. Marouane Fellaini and Wayne Rooney
8. Joleon Lescott
9. Martin Keown
10. Romelu Lukaku

QUIZ No.6 AWAY FROM GOODISON (BEFORE)

1. Howard Kendall
2. Tim Cahill
3. James Beattie
4. Yannick Bolasie
5. Gareth Barry
6. Paul Gascoigne and Vinny Samways
7. Norman Whiteside
8. Dennis Stevens
9. Paul Power
10. Alessandro Pistone

QUIZ No.7 THE 'B' TEAM

1. Jesper Blomqvist
2. Earl Barrett
3. John Bailey
4. Slaven Bilic
5. James Beattie
6. Leighton Baines
7. David Burrows
8. Paul Bracewell
9. Peter Beagrie
10. Gareth Barry

QUIZ No.8 BIRTHPLACES

1. Martin Keown – who was born in Oxford
2. Seamus Coleman – who was born in Donegal
3. Duncan Ferguson – who was born in Stirling
4. Manchester
5. Mike Bernard – who was born in Shrewsbury
6. Cahill – Sydney, Pistone – Milan, Pienaar – Johannesburg, McCall – Leeds
7. James Vaughan

8. Newcastle and Bradford
9. Darron Gibson – born in Derry
10. England lost there in 1950 in the World Cup to the USA

QUIZ No.9 CAPTAINCY

1. Kevin Ratcliffe
2. Phil Neville
3. Johnny Holt and Jimmy Galt
4. Dixie Dean and Roy Vernon
5. Mike Lyons
6. Brian Labone
7. Warney Cresswell and T.G. Jones
8. Dave Watson
9. Jack Taylor
10. Alan Ball

QUIZ No.10 COUNTRIES OF ORIGIN - PART 1

1. Colombia
2. Brazil
3. Portugal
4. Iceland
5. Italy
6. Zimbabwe
7. USA
8. Ivory Coast
9. Costa Rica
10. Holland

QUIZ No.11 COUNTRIES OF ORIGIN - PART 2

1. France
2. Nigeria
3. Germany
4. Belgium
5. Croatia
6. Greece
7. Denmark
8. Poland
9. Spain
10. Argentina

QUIZ No.12 CRYPTIC BLUES - PART 1

1. Jimmy Husband
2. Gordon West
3. Keith Newton
4. Henry Newton
5. Michael Branch
6. Alan and Michael Ball
7. Graeme Sharp
8. Bryan Hamilton
9. Harry Catterick
10. Wally Fielding

QUIZ No.13 CRYPTIC BLUES - PART 2

1. Albert Dunlop
2. Joe Royle
3. Don Donovan
4. Fred Pickering
5. Jimmy Gabriel
6. Alex Scott
7. George Martin
8. Neville Southall
9. Roy Vernon
10. George Jackson

QUIZ No.14 CRYPTIC BLUES - PART 3

1. Duncan Ferguson
2. Richard Wright
3. Gary Stanley
4. Derek Temple
5. Tommy Fleetwood
6. Bert Rigsby
7. Alan Stubbs
8. Darron Gibson
9. Colin Harvey
10. Dixie Dean

QUIZ No.15 CRYPTIC BLUES - PART 4

1. Mike Lyons
2. Hugh Bolton
3. Gareth Barry
4. Dan Gosling
5. Tony Kay
6. Eddie Wainwright
7. Gary Speed
8. Jordan Pickford
9. George Kitchen
10. Seamus Coleman

QUIZ No.16 EVERTON IN EUROPE 1962-95 - CLUBS

1. Dunfermline and Kilmarnock
2. Manchester United
3. Inter Milan
4. Finn Harps
5. Feyenoord
6. Rapid Vienna
7. Bayern Munich
8. Borussia Moenchengladbach and Panathinaikos
9. Aalborg
10. Milan

QUIZ No.17 EVERTON IN EUROPE 1962-95 - PLAYERS

1. Dennis Stevens
2. Fred Pickering
3. Sandy Brown
4. Alan Ball
5. David Unsworth
6. Jimmy Gabriel
7. Andy Gray
8. Paul Bracewell
9. Derek Temple, Andy Gray, Graeme Sharp and Paul Rideout
10. Daniel Amokachi and Alex Young

QUIZ No.18 EVERTON IN EUROPE - THE 21ST CENTURY - CLUBS

1. Villareal
2. Brann
3. Fiorentina
4. Standard Liege
5. Benfica
6. AEK Athens
7. Sporting Lisbon
8. Wolfsburg
9. Dynamo Kiev
10. Atalanta

QUIZ No.19 EVERTON IN EUROPE - THE 21ST CENTURY - PLAYERS

1. James Beattie
2. Jo
3. Arteta, Baines and Lukaku
4. Joseph Yobo
5. Yakubu and Lukaku
6. James Vaughan
7. Victor Anichebe
8. Lukaku
9. Joleon Lescott and Tim Cahill
10. Bilyaletdinov

QUIZ No.20 EVERTON IN THE FA CUP 1892-1939

1. Derby County
2. Sheffield Wednesday
3. Southampton
4. Jarrow
5. Jimmy Settle got a hat-trick
6. Bell, Bolton and Browell
7. Crystal Palace
8. Fulham
9. He was the youngest-ever league player, at 15 years 158 days on 16 September 1929 v Millwall
10. Tommy Lawton

QUIZ No.21 EVERTON IN THE FA CUP 1945-60

1. Preston North End
2. Sheffield Wednesday
3. Aston Villa
4. Sunderland
5. West Ham United and Southend United
6. Dave Hickson
7. Liverpool and Sheffield Wednesday
8. Fulham and Leyton Orient
9. Blackburn Rovers
10. QPR, West Ham United and Spurs

QUIZ No.22 EVERTON IN CUP COMPETITIONS - THE 1960s

1. Sheffield United
2. West Ham United
3. Manchester City and Sunderland
4. Kings Lynn and Bedford Town
5. Frank Wignall
6. Bristol City
7. Johnny Morrissey
8. Fred Pickering
9. Roy Vernon
10. 3-1

QUIZ No.23 EVERTON IN CUP COMPETITIONS - THE 1970s

1. They never played away from home
2. Altrincham
3. Arsenal
4. Notts County and Nottingham Forest
5. Middlesbrough
6. Spurs, Millwall, Fulham and West Ham United
7. Wimbledon
8. Aston Villa
9. Bolton Wanderers
10. Sheffield

QUIZ No.24 EVERTON IN CUP COMPETITIONS - THE 1980s

1. Aston Villa and Arsenal
2. Newport County
3. Grimsby Town
4. West Ham United and Wimbledon
5. Oxford United, Adrian Heath and Howard Kendall
6. Shrewsbury Town
7. Arsenal
8. Sheffield Wednesday
9. Graeme Sharp
10. Liverpool

QUIZ No.25 EVERTON IN CUP COMPETITIONS - THE 1990s
1. Jurgen Klinsmann
2. Newcastle United and Exeter City
3. Bristol City
4. Chelsea
5. Sunderland
6. Graham Stuart and Tony Cottee
7. Norwich City
8. Wrexham
9. Watford and Wolves
10. Portsmouth, Millwall and York City

QUIZ No.26 EVERTON IN THE LEAGUE 1888-1939
1. Accrington and Anfield
2. Derby County
3. Preston North End
4. Oldham Athletic
5. Chelsea
6. The games were played in sets of twos – home and away
7. Nine
8. West Brom
9. Six
10. Aston Villa and Sunderland

QUIZ No.27 EVERTON IN THE LEAGUE 1946-60
1. Eddie Wainwright
2. None
3. Portsmouth
4. They lost 6-0 but it didn't stop Wednesday being relegated with them
5. Huddersfield Town
6. Tommy Eglington
7. 8-4
8. Sheffield United
9. Spurs and Jimmy Harris
10. Newcastle United

QUIZ No.28 EVERTON IN THE LEAGUE - THE 1960s
1. Bobby Collins
2. Cardiff City
3. C – 42
4. Fred Pickering
5. 5-4 to Everton
6. Fulham
7. Leicester City
8. They were Royle and Husband
9. Vernon, Pickering, Ball and Royle
10. Albert Dunlop and Gordon West

QUIZ No.29 EVERTON IN THE LEAGUE - THE 1970s
1. Southampton
2. Joe Royle with four and David Johnson with three
3. Bob Latchford
4. Leicester City and QPR
5. Duncan McKenzie
6. B – 6-0
7. Bristol City
8. Leeds United
9. George Wood
10. Mike Lyons

QUIZ No.30 EVERTON IN THE LEAGUE - THE 1980s
1. Crystal Palace and Coventry City
2. C – Luton Town
3. Vicarage Road, Watford
4. 16
5. Nottingham Forest and Manchester United
6. Arsenal and Southampton
7. Wayne Clarke
8. The Dell, Southampton
9. Sixth
10. Aston Villa

QUIZ No.31 EVERTON IN THE LEAGUE - THE 1990s
1. Two
2. Robert Warzycha
3. Peter Beardsley and Tony Cottee
4. Manchester City
5. Sheffield United and Swindon Town
6. Wimbledon – Stuart (2) and Horne
7. Andrei Kanchelskis
8. Southampton
9. Bolton Wanderers
10. Mark and Stephen Hughes

QUIZ No.32 EVERTON V LIVERPOOL - LEAGUE AND FA CUP 1894-1939
1. October
2. Everton
3. 2-1 to Liverpool at Goodison
4. Sandy Young
5. Villa Park
6. 11
7. Bobby Parker
8. 3-3
9. Dean and Martin
10. Tommy Lawton

QUIZ No.33 EVERTON V LIVERPOOL - CUP COMPETITIONS - 1946-90

1. Two
2. The third and the sixth
3. Alan Ball
4. Stuart McCall
5. Anfield
6. Bryan Hamilton and Clive Thomas
7. Duncan McKenzie and Bruce Rioch
8. Gary Lineker
9. Peter Eastoe and Imre Varadi
10. West Brom

QUIZ No.34 EVERTON V LIVERPOOL - CUP COMPETITIONS - 1990-2020

1. Pat Nevin
2. Tony Cottee
3. Graeme Sharp and Peter Beardsley
4. Dave Watson
5. Joleon Lescott
6. Dan Gosling
7. The TV coverage missed the goal by going to an advert!
8. Nikica Jelavic
9. Gylfi Sigurdsson
10. Neither – they never met

QUIZ No.35 EVERTON V LIVERPOOL - THE LEAGUE 1946-90

1. 0-0
2. Eddie Wainwright
3. Roy Vernon
4. Johnny Morrissey and Derek Temple
5. Alan Ball and Sandy Brown
6. Joe Royle and Alan Whittle
7. Howard Kendall and Andy King
8. It was the only season in which both games ended 0-0
9. Paul Wilkinson and Wayne Clarke
10. Graeme Sharp

QUIZ No.36 EVERTON V LIVERPOOL - THE LEAGUE - 1990-2020

1. Peter Beardsley and Mo Johnston
2. Andrei Kanchelskis
3. Kevin Campbell
4. Lee Carsley
5. 3-0
6. Tim Cahill and Mikel Arteta
7. Kevin Mirallas

8. Phil Jagielka
9. Wayne Rooney
10. 0-0

QUIZ No.37 EVERTONIANS

1. Judi Dench
2. Bill Dean
3. Martin Dwyer
4. Austin Healey
5. Tony Blackburn
6. Tony Bellew
7. Sylvester Stallone
8. Susan George
9. John Parrott
10. Pete Best

QUIZ No.38 EVERTON - SEASON 2000/01

1. Duncan Ferguson
2. Franny Jeffers
3. Danny Cadamarteri and Kevin Campbell
4. West Ham United and Aston Villa
5. Bristol Rovers
6. Tranmere Rovers
7. Kevin Campbell
8. David Weir
9. St. James' Park
10. Leicester City

QUIZ No.39 EVERTON - SEASON 2001/02

1. Six
2. 17
3. Jesper Blomqvist
4. Crystal Palace
5. Middlesbrough
6. Walter Smith
7. Kevin Campbell
8. West Ham United
9. Southampton
10. Nick Chadwick

QUIZ No.40 EVERTON - SEASON 2002/03

1. Mark Pembridge
2. Wrexham
3. Newcastle United
4. Chelsea
5. They finished 92nd in the league
6. 1-0
7. 2-1
8. Brian McBride
9. Tomasz Radzinski
10. Alan Stubbs

QUIZ No.41 EVERTON – SEASON 2003/04
1. Portsmouth
2. Manchester United
3. Manchester City
4. Southampton
5. Duncan Ferguson
6. Middlesbrough
7. Fulham
8. Franny Jeffers
9. Steve Watson
10. Elland Road

QUIZ No.42 EVERTON – SEASON 2004/05
1. 1987/88
2. Kevin Kilbane
3. 12
4. Yakubu and McBride
5. Plymouth Argyle and Preston North End
6. Tim Cahill
7. Thomas Gravesen
8. Gary Neville and Paul Scholes
9. Duncan Ferguson
10. Matt Holland

QUIZ No.43 EVERTON – SEASON 2005/06
1. None
2. Marcus Bent
3. James Beattie
4. Leon Osman
5. Craven Cottage
6. Millwall
7. Chelsea
8. Middlesbrough
9. West Brom and Aston Villa
10. Six

QUIZ No.44 EVERTON – SEASON 2006/07
1. Joseph Yobo and Lee Carsley
2. Andy Johnson
3. James Beattie and Mikel Arteta
4. Spurs
5. Phil Neville
6. James McFadden
7. Peterborough United and Luton Town
8. Blackburn Rovers
9. Eight
10. Tony Hibbert

QUIZ No.45 EVERTON – SEASON 2007/08
1. Sunderland
2. Yakubu
3. Joleon Lescott
4. Phil Jagielka
5. Oldham Athletic
6. Sheffield Wednesday, Luton Town and West Ham United
7. Chelsea
8. 11 – 4 – 4
9. Fulham
10. Nicklas Bendtner

QUIZ No.46 EVERTON – SEASON 2008/09
1. 1914–15
2. They were scored by eight different players
3. Lucas
4. Cahill missed and Jagielka scored the winning penalty
5. Gareth Barry
6. Tim Cahill
7. Blackburn Rovers
8. Theo Walcott
9. John Terry and Kevin Nolan
10. Arteta and Jo

QUIZ No.47 EVERTON – SEASON 2009/10
1. 6-1
2. Louis Saha
3. Birmingham City and Spurs
4. Tim Howard
5. Hull City
6. Mikel Arteta
7. Leighton Baines
8. Landon Donovan
9. Roberto Mancini
10. Diniyar Bilyaletdinov

QUIZ No.48 EVERTON – SEASON 2010/11
1. Blackpool and Louis Saha
2. Tim Cahill and Mikel Arteta
3. 5-1
4. Chelsea and Brentford
5. Manchester City
6. Jermaine Beckford
7. Tim Cahill
8. Phil Jagielka and Tony Hibbert
9. Reading
10. Marouane Fellaini and Mikel Arteta

QUIZ No.49 EVERTON – SEASON 2011/12
1. Nikica Jelavic
2. Leighton Baines
3. Nikica Jelavic and Steven Pienaar
4. Tamworth
5. Phil Neville
6. They were drawn at home for all seven ties
7. Darron Gibson – it was against Manchester City
8. Aaron Lennon
9. Leon Osman
10. Apostolos Vellios and Royston Drenthe

QUIZ No.50 EVERTON – SEASON 2012/13
1. Manchester United
2. Chelsea
3. Leighton Baines
4. Arouna Kone
5. Both goals were own goals
6. Marouane Fellaini
7. Leyton Orient and Leeds United
8. Steven Pienaar and Nikica Jelavic
9. Gylfi Sigurdsson
10. Johnny Heitinga

QUIZ No.51 EVERTON – SEASON 2013/14
1. The most points in a Premier League season
2. Romelu Lukaku
3. QPR and Fulham
4. Seamus Coleman
5. Stevenage Town
6. Score an own goal
7. West Ham United
8. Bryan Oviedo
9. He got the sack after the game
10. Mikel Arteta

QUIZ No.52 EVERTON – SEASON 2014/15
1. Samuel Eto'o
2. Aiden McGeady
3. Yannick Bolasie
4. John Stones
5. Joel Robles
6. Gylfi Sigurdsson
7. Romelu Lukaku
8. Phil Jagielka
9. Jonjo Shelvey
10. Nikica Jelavic

QUIZ No.53 EVERTON – SEASON 2015/16
1. Sunderland
2. Six
3. Ross Barkley
4. Gary Lineker
5. Steven Naismith
6. Bournemouth
7. Morgan Schneiderlin and Wayne Rooney
8. Tom Cleverley
9. Gareth Barry and Diego Costa
10. Tim Howard

QUIZ No.54 EVERTON – SEASON 2016/17
1. 1989/90
2. Bournemouth – 6-3
3. Nine
4. Arouna Kone
5. Steven Naismith
6. Gareth Barry
7. Leicester City
8. Shay Given and David Marshall
9. Ademola Lookman
10. Matthew Pennington

QUIZ No.55 EVERTON – SEASON 2017/18
1. Arsenal and Ronald Koeman
2. Huddersfield Town
3. Eighth
4. Stoke City and Manchester City
5. Oumar Niasse
6. Leighton Baines from the penalty spot
7. Richarlison
8. West Ham United
9. Theo Walcott
10. Cenk Tosun

QUIZ No.56 EVERTON – SEASON 2018/19
1. Phil Jagielka
2. Richarlison and Sigurdsson
3. Spurs and Burnley
4. Millwall
5. Dominic Calvert-Lewin
6. Theo Walcott
7. Lucas Digne
8. Yerry Mina
9. Kurt Zouma
10. Jordan Pickford

QUIZ No.57 EVERTON – SEASON 2019/20

1. Liverpool
2. 12th
3. Calvert-Lewin and Richarlison
4. Mason Holgate
5. Leicester City
6. Yerry Mina
7. Manchester United
8. Michael Keane
9. Norwich City
10. Bournemouth

QUIZ No.58 EVERTON – SEASON 2020/21

1. West Brom and Brighton
2. Spurs, Crystal Palace and Dominic Calvert-Lewin
3. Richarlison and Digne
4. Mina and Keane
5. Richarlison and Sigurdsson
6. West Ham United and West Brom
7. Richarlison
8. Moise Kean and Michael Keane
9. Spurs
10. Bernard

QUIZ No.59 EVERY LITTLE HELPS (OWN GOALS)

1. Matthew Upson
2. Jack Cork
3. John Terry
4. Chris Smalling
5. Ryan Shawcross
6. Ben Mee
7. Laurent Koscielny
8. Kyle Naughton
9. Adam Webster
10. Victor Lindelof

QUIZ No.60 THE FA CUP FINALS OF 1893, 1897, 1906, 1907 & 1933

1. Wolves
2. Aston Villa
3. Newcastle United
4. Young
5. Sheffield Wednesday
6. Sharp
7. Manchester City
8. The players' shirts had numbers on their backs for the first time
9. True
10. True – the first crowd was 45,000 and the second was 92,950

QUIZ No.61 THE FA CUP FINALS OF 1966, 1968, 1984 & 1985

1. Sheffield Wednesday and 3-2
2. Mike Trebilcock
3. Young – Alex and Gerry
4. West Brom
5. Amber shirts and blue shorts
6. West, Wright, Wilson – the first time in any FA Cup final that the goalkeeper and two full-backs began with the same letter
7. Watford and Andy Gray
8. Peter Reid
9. John Gidman
10. Paul Bracewell

QUIZ No.62 THE FA CUP FINALS OF 1986, 1989, 1995 & 2009

1. Gary Lineker
2. Trevor Steven and Gary Stevens
3. Pat Van den Hauwe, Kevin Ratcliffe, Trevor Steven, Paul Bracewell and Kevin Sheedy
4. Stuart McCall – the first time a scorer of two goals in an FA Cup final finished on the losing side on the day
5. Gary Ablett, Steve McMahon and Peter Beardsley
6. Paul Rideout
7. Dave Watson
8. Louis Saha
9. 25 Seconds
10. Tim Howard and Phil Neville

QUIZ No.63 FA CUP SEMI-FINALS

1. They've won 13 and lost 13
2. West Ham United
3. Derby County
4. Liverpool – five times
5. Manchester United
6. Six
7. Southampton
8. Barnsley, Leeds United and Sheffield Wednesday
9. John Willie Parker and Daniel Amokachi
10. Manchester United and Arsenal

QUIZ No.64 GOALKEEPERS

1. Dave Lawson
2. Albert Dunlop
3. Gordon West
4. Bobby Mimms
5. Jimmy O'Neill

6. Ted Sagar
7. Dai Davies
8. Espen Baardsen – the bonus was Bruce Grobbelaar
9. Andy Rankin
10. Bill Scott

QUIZ No.65 GOODISON PARK - PART 1
1. Walton
2. Nottingham Forest
3. Fred Geary
4. Manchester United
5. Sunderland
6. Scotland
7. The 1980s
8. Dixie Dean
9. Turnstile fraud
10. West Germany and the USSR

QUIZ No.66 GOODISON PARK - PART 2
1. John Houlding
2. Mere Green Field
3. Notts County
4. 1910
5. West Brom
6. Brazil
7. 1948
8. Floodlights and undersoil heating
9. Eusebio
10. They remained unbeaten at home all that season

QUIZ No.67 IF THE CAP FITS - PART 1
1. Tony Kay, Derek Temple, Colin Harvey, David Unsworth and Michael Ball
2. Leon Osman
3. Brian Labone and Joleon Lescott
4. Phil Jagielka
5. Nick Barmby
6. Leighton Baines
7. Keith Newton and Fred Pickering
8. Martin Dobson
9. Bob Latchford
10. John Stones

QUIZ No.68 IF THE CAP FITS - PART 2
1. George Wood
2. Mick Meagan
3. 13
4. Scott Gemmill

5. Kevin Kilbane
6. Asa Hartford and Bryan Hamilton
7. Dai and Simon Davies
8. Bobby and John Collins
9. Ashley Williams
10. Gary Naysmith and Steven Naismith

QUIZ No.69 MANAGERS - PART 1
1. Mike Walker
2. Howard Kendall
3. Walter Smith
4. Ronald Koeman
5. Carlo Ancelotti and Rafa Benitez
6. Johnny Carey
7. Luton Town
8. They all managed Blackburn Rovers
9. Dick Molyneux
10. Gordon Lee

QUIZ No.70 MANAGERS - PART 2
1. True
2. Watford and Hull City
3. Cliff Britton
4. Jimmy Gabriel, David Unsworth, Duncan Ferguson and Dave Watson
5. Roberto Martinez and Rafa Benitez
6. Thomas McIntosh
7. Bill Cuff
8. Colin Harvey
9. Preston North End
10. Howard Kendall

QUIZ No.71 MULTIPLE CHOICE
1. A – West Brom
2. C – Tim Howard
3. C – Gary Stevens
4. A – Blackburn Rovers
5. D – Newcastle United
6. B – Peter Schmeichel
7. C – Bob Latchford
8. B – Nicky Barmby
9. D – John Ebbrell
10. A – Sheffield United

QUIZ No.72 THE NINE - PART 1
1. Manchester United, Liverpool and Arsenal
2. 1969/70
3. False – Arsenal won four
4. Seven
5. Trevor Steven
6. 12
7. Dixie Dean

8. Roy Vernon, Joe Royle and Graeme Sharp
9. Fred Geary and Dixie Dean
10. Arsenal and Spurs

QUIZ No.73 THE NINE - PART 2
1. Everton held it over two world wars – 20 years to Liverpool's 19
2. Tommy Lawton and Trevor Steven
3. 1914/15
4. Wolves
5. 22
6. Huddersfield Town and Leeds United
7. 66 and 90
8. Liverpool
9. 1931/32
10. 1890/91

QUIZ No.74 OPENING DAYS
1. Spurs
2. Hull City
3. Nottingham Forest and Southampton
4. Plymouth Argyle
5. Derek Temple and Alan Ball
6. Sheffield Wednesday three times and United once
7. White Hart Lane
8. Derby County
9. Tony Cottee
10. Leeds United

QUIZ No.75 POST-WAR HAT-TRICKS
1. Southampton
2. John Willie Parker
3. Manchester City, Birmingham City and Southampton
4. Adrian Heath
5. Crystal Palace, Wimbledon and QPR
6. Paul Wilkinson
7. Ephraim 'Jock' Dodds
8. Fulham
9. Kevin Campbell
10. Nick Barmby

QUIZ No.76 POT LUCK
1. One is Craig Short and the other is David Smallman
2. Geoff Barnett
3. Bolton Wanderers and West Ham United – they both lost to Liverpool
4. Blue-and-white stripes and all black
5. Tommy Clinton
6. Martin Keown and Mike Newell
7. Alan Ball
8. Newcastle United and Watford
9. Brearley
10. Aston Villa

QUIZ No.77 SEEING RED AGAINST THE BLUES
1. Fabricio Coloccini, Jamaal Lascelles and Jonjo Shelvey
2. Ashley Barnes
3. Tom Huddlestone
4. Kyle Walker
5. Anthony Knockaert
6. Charlie Adam
7. Maya Yoshida
8. Wes Morgan
9. Willy Boly
10. Son Heung-min

QUIZ No.78 STICKY TOFFEE (SENT-OFF)
1. James McFadden
2. Tim Cahill
3. Kevin Kilbane
4. James Beattie
5. Diniyar Bilyaletdinov
6. Seamus Coleman
7. Steven Pienaar
8. Duncan Ferguson
9. Darron Gibson
10. Jack Rodwell

QUIZ No.79 STICKY TOFFEE (MORE, ANYONE?)
1. Lucas Digne
2. James McCarthy
3. Ashley Williams
4. Idrissa Gueye
5. Richarlison
6. Morgan Schneiderlin
7. Kevin Mirallas
8. Gareth Barry
9. Kurt Zouma
10. Ramiro Funes-Mori

QUIZ No.80 TOP TOFFEES - No.1 - ALAN BALL
1. Blackpool. Arsenal, Southampton and Bristol Rovers
2. Fulham
3. 250
4. Molineux
5. West Brom

6. Darlington and Sheffield United
7. True
8. Hurst and Peters
9. Belgium
10. Portsmouth

QUIZ No.81 TOP TOFFEES - No.2 - DIXIE DEAN

1. Tranmere Rovers and Notts County
2. Highbury
3. George Camsell
4. Aston Villa and Birmingham City
5. Sheffield – United away and Wednesday at home
6. Newcastle United
7. A – Charlton Athletic
8. Leicester City
9. Score a hat-trick on more than one occasion
10. Arsenal

QUIZ No.82 TOP TOFFEES - No.3 - PETER FARRELL

1. Johnny Carey
2. The Victoria Ground, Stoke
3. Blackburn Rovers
4. False – he scored in a 3-1 defeat at Anfield on Christmas Eve 1949
5. Chelsea and West Ham United
6. Bolton Wanderers
7. Goodison Park – it was England's first defeat on home soil by a team from outside the British Isles
8. True
9. Tranmere Rovers
10. Tommy Eglington

QUIZ No.83 TOP TOFFEES - No.4 - COLIN HARVEY

1. The San Siro – Inter Milan
2. Anfield
3. Sheffield Wednesday
4. Joe Royle
5. Manchester United
6. West Brom
7. Ten and six
8. Chelsea
9. Upton Park and Selhurst Park
10. He took the job as Kendall's assistant when he would have felt very conflicted

QUIZ No.84 TOP TOFFEES - No.5 - HOWARD KENDALL

1. Preston North End, Birmingham City, Stoke City and Blackburn Rovers
2. West Ham United
3. Leicester City
4. Liverpool and Newcastle United
5. Colchester United and Spurs
6. Chelsea
7. Birmingham City and Coventry City
8. Gordon Lee, Colin Harvey and Joe Royle
9. Manchester City, Blackburn Rovers, Sheffield United and Notts County
10. Greece – Xanthi and Ethnikos Piraeus

QUIZ No.85 TOP TOFFEES - No.6 - BRIAN LABONE

1. At the age of 27 he gave notice of his retirement, but was eventually talked out of it
2. Birmingham City
3. Blackburn Rovers and Burnley
4. True
5. Roger Kenyon
6. They captained the FA Cup winners of 1965 and 1967 and Brian was the winning captain in 1966
7. Five – awesome stuff!
8. Ray Wilson
9. Leon – the player was Leon Osman
10. Kevin Ratcliffe

QUIZ No.86 TOP TOFFEES - No.7 - KEVIN RATCLIFFE

1. Old Trafford
2. Ninian Park and Cardiff Arms Park
3. True
4. Carrow Road and Anfield
5. They were both scored on the 22nd of the month
6. False – he played all 42 in 1986/87
7. Cardiff City
8. Dundee and Derby County
9. Chester City
10. Shrewsbury Town – David Moyes used to play for Shrewsbury

QUIZ No.87 TOP TOFFEES - No.8 - PETER REID
1. Bolton Wanderers and QPR
2. 13
3. West Ham United
4. Nottingham
5. Fortuna Sittard
6. Ray Wilkins and Bryan Robson
7. Spurs
8. Shrewsbury Town and Telford United
9. Selhurst Park
10. Manchester City

QUIZ No.88 TOP TOFFEES - No.9 - NEVILLE SOUTHALL
1. Bert Trautmann, Gordon Banks and Pat Jennings
2. The number is 747
3. Chris Gunter
4. Torquay United
5. Bradford City and Leeds United
6. Ipswich Town
7. Seven
8. Four and four
9. Bobby Gould and Mark Hughes
10. Dover Athletic, Hastings United and Margate

QUIZ No.89 TOP TOFFEES - No.10 - ROY VERNON
1. Blackburn Rovers
2. True
3. Stoke City and Halifax Town
4. Scotland
5. Stan Bentham
6. Bobby Collins and Tony Kay
7. D – Walsall
8. Highbury
9. Leeds United
10. They all came on the final home game of the season – leave them smiling!

QUIZ No.90 TOP TOFFEES - No.11 - DAVE WATSON
1. Norwich City and Tranmere Rovers
2. Less – £900,000
3. Nottingham Forest and Spurs
4. The League Cup with Norwich City in 1985
5. Brazil
6. Sheffield Wednesday
7. Crystal Palace

8. Liverpool and Newcastle United
9. West Ham United
10. Liverpool

QUIZ No.91 TOP TOFFEES - No.12 - ALEX YOUNG
1. The Golden Vision
2. 1962/63
3. Hearts and George Thomson
4. Ray Wilson
5. Republic of Ireland
6. Blackburn Rovers and Blackpool
7. Shrewsbury Town and Sunderland
8. Sheffield Wednesday
9. Burnley
10. Old Trafford and Stockport County

QUIZ No.92 TRANSFERS - 1888-1950
1. Blackpool
2. Tommy Booth
3. He scored the winning goal in the 1914 FA Cup final against Liverpool
4. Charlie Crossley
5. He played in goal in an emergency for New Brighton against Hartlepools United in the Third Division North on 15 March 1947
6. Jimmy Dunn
7. Blackburn Rovers and Burnley
8. Tory
9. Bob Kelso
10. Alec Troup

QUIZ No.93 TRANSFERS - 1951-1989
1. Dave Clements
2. Alec Ashworth
3. George Cummins
4. Neil Pointon
5. Derby County
6. Dave Thomas
7. Crystal Palace
8. Asa Hartford and Bolton Wanderers
9. Alan Harper
10. Brian Godfrey

QUIZ No.94 TRANSFERS - 1990-2005
1. Tony Cottee
2. Andy Hinchcliffe
3. Barry Horne

4. John Oster
5. Gary Speed
6. John Collins
7. Mike Newell
8. Steve Watson
9. James McFadden
10. Kevin Kilbane

QUIZ No.95 TRANSFERS - 2006-20

1. John Stones and Mason Holgate
2. Joleon Lescott
3. Jermaine Beckford
4. Phil Jagielka and Dominic Calvert-Lewin
5. Ashley Williams
6. Yakubu
7. Andy Johnson
8. Alex Iwobi
9. Charlton Athletic
10. Sylvain Distin

QUIZ No.96 TRUE OR FALSE

1. True
2. True
3. False – Alan Ball did
4. False – they did it twice to Arsenal in the 1930s
5. True
6. False – it was Portsmouth, not Southampton
7. False – fourth
8. True
9. False – Freeman scored 38 in 1908/09
10. True

QUIZ No.97 VENUES

1. The Crystal Palace
2. Manchester – the grounds are Fallowfield, Maine Road and Old Trafford
3. Villa Park
4. Trent Bridge
5. Highbury
6. Maine Road
7. Leeds United
8. Burnden Park, Bolton
9. Elland Road
10. Bramall Lane and Ewood Park

QUIZ No.98 WHERE DID YOU COME FROM?

1. Real Sociedad
2. Borussia Dortmund and Hamburg
3. Trabzonspor
4. Yerry Mina, Lucas Digne and Andre Gomes
5. San Jose Clash and New England Revolution
6. Atletico Madrid
7. Spartak Moscow and Lokomotiv Moscow
8. Anderlecht and Bruges
9. PSV Eindhoven
10. Standard Liege

QUIZ No.99 WILD CARD - PART 1

1. Bolton Wanderers
2. Tommy Wright, Keith Newton, Brian Labone and Alan Ball
3. Spurs and Manchester United
4. Chelsea, Fulham and Wimbledon
5. David Ginola
6. Jones – Dave and Gary
7. Billy Bingham
8. Terry Darracott
9. Samuel Eto'o and Wayne Rooney
10. He was born in Hastings

QUIZ No.100 WILD CARD - PART 2

1. The FA Youth Cup
2. Roger Kenyon
3. Derek Temple was missing and Joe Royle and Johnny Morrissey were additions
4. The Full Members' Cup
5. Bellefield and Finch Farm
6. Alex 'Sandy' Young
7. Bramley Moore Dock
8. C – 52,888
9. 29
10. Brian Kidd